15 March 1986
C.M.Leslie

BIRDS AND THEIR YOUNG

Uniform with this Volume

BIRDS IN FLIGHT

BY
W. P. PYCRAFT, F.Z.S.

Illustrated by
ROLAND GREEN, F.Z.S.

Containing 12 plates in colour and
17 illustrations in black and white

BIRDS
ONE SHOULD KNOW
BENEFICIAL AND MISCHIEVOUS

BY
THE REV. CANON THEODORE WOOD

Illustrated by
ROLAND GREEN, F.Z.S.

Containing 8 plates in colour and 16 plates
in black and white

Robins.

CONTENTS

ILLUSTRATIONS

COLOURED PLATES

PEN AND INK PLATES

BIRDS AND THEIR YOUNG

CHAPTER I

INTRODUCTORY

A Eulogy of Birds: Undoubtedly birds attracted attention when the world was very young, and there is every reason to believe that something more than a desire to utilise their gastronomic qualities impelled primitive man to trap them or slay them with stick or stone; he admired their plumage. The fashion of wearing feathers is many thousands of years old, and, however much we object to the destruction and cruelty associated with the plumage trade, we must admit that it is an ancient business, an effort to supply a demand. Primitive man wore beautiful feathers, uncivilised man wears them to-day; those who exploit birds for purposes of profit are keeping up a barbarous custom, and those women who persist in demanding these decorations retain primitive or barbarous instincts, but we cannot say that they are inartistic.

Fortunately, there is an ever-growing love of the beautiful in Nature, and true love cannot be separated from consideration and mercy; the more we love the beautiful in Nature the more we shall desire to preserve it. The brilliant and beautiful feather is very much more attractive when in place on the living bird than when stuck in the woolly locks of even a handsome Polynesian, or trailing from the latest "creation" of the milliner.

The artist cannot define Beauty; he can only explain what appeals to him as beautiful. The physicist cannot even define colour, though he can show how it is affected by light. The psychologist is not certain if colour or beauty exist at all. But the naturalist does not trouble about these details, for he sees beauty in all natural objects, often in those humble creatures or despised "weeds" which others have the audacity to call "ugly." Nevertheless, whatever our particular taste, whatever we call interesting or beautiful, we must admit that there is universal admiration for certain colours, shapes, forms, or arrangements of markings, that instinctively suggests beauty. In the Vegetable Kingdom the flower appeals; in the Animal the bird. The individual leaf or the massed foliage, the grace and strength of the tree, the elegance of the fern, or the dainty structure of the moss or lichen, naturally excites wonder and admiration; the lines of the horse, the sleek softness of the fur-clothed cat, the marvellous colour-pattern of the glorious butterfly, the pink-tinged shell upon the beach, or the glistening of the fresh-caught salmon, stimulate thrills of pleasure; but if we ask—"what are the most beautiful natural objects?" nine out of ten will reply, "the flower and the bird."

The child knows, and the child is father of the man. It is the flower that first attracts the staggering infant; it is the bird to which its chubby fingers point. In the yet undeveloped brain is an inherited desire to touch, to possess the beautiful, and these are what it feels rather than knows are beautiful.

At present we are not concerned with the flower, but we wish to discover what it is in the bird that rouses instinctive admiration. It might be argued that it is the possession of functionable wings, the ability to fly, which, without artificial aids, is impossible to man, that puts them in a world beyond our ken. But what about the fly, the butterfly, the beetle? Many of these insects excel the bird in air-mastery; what bird, for instance, can control an aerial side-dart like that of the hover-fly? No, in the matter of wings and how to use them, we must own that the hand-winged bat and the dragon-fly successfully compete with many birds. The texture, colour, and general arrangement of feather or feathers undoubtedly has influence, and the neatness of pattern, combination of shades, and conspicuous markings attract even the casual eye. And, without doubt, the habit of so many birds of producing sounds that have a pleasing effect upon the human ear is much in the bird's favour; song, bird song, is one of the greatest of Nature's lavish gifts. Yet it is not every bird whose voice is harmonious, at any rate to our ears; the peacock, for instance, would not get much applause in a concert hall, however much he earned upon the stage. No, it is not one quality alone that makes birds attractive, but many, and not the least of their varied qualities is that of familiarity.

No doubt it sounds absurd to say that many shy and retiring kinds are familiar; they are not, if we mean by that, that they are friendly. But if we speak of birds in general as familiar objects, the term will be understood. We have known birds since we were infants, and we have fondly imagined that we knew something about them—they lay eggs in nests, they fly and they sing; they come in winter to be fed, typical mendicants. But how much do we really know about their life, and how much about their outlook on life, even of their opinion of us? There are scores of questions which the most accomplished ornithologist cannot answer. In the following pages it may be that certain facts related about birds and their young, tracing their life from its beginning to maturity, may give us clues that will help to solve some of the problems that still puzzle the learned.

Infancy : The Infancy of birds is a fascinating study, but as a study it must consist in something more than looking at, even admiring, young birds ; they have engaging habits, certainly, but we must try to understand what those habits mean to them, and what good they derive from them.

To discover this we must trace the life-story from its beginnings—and watch the parent and the young, for the one without the other is incomplete.

However much the cynic may declare that some people—less ethereal, than Peter Pan—never grow up, there are stages in the life of man. " His acts being seven ages " is a wonderful analysis. More or less correctly we can estimate when infancy passes to childhood, youth to maturity, and old age to senility, but with birds slight observation shows great variation, not only in the length of life of a species but in the age at which it becomes mature. But there is something more than this, for all birds do not become infants at the same age ! The fact is, that the bird begins its life apart from its mother within that hard but brittle envelope, the egg-shell.

To state that birds are descended from reptiles, and then draw comparisons between birds as we know them and reptiles of to-day, is not what science teaches, although such statements are made in loosely written pseudo-scientific books. There was, of course, in the history of the world, an age when there were no birds, nor were there at that time any reptiles, and it is doubtful if there were dinosaurs, reptile-like creatures all now extinct. But there existed some ancestral form from which all three descended in that age-long period of change in which we trace

KITTIWAKE.

the Evolution of our modern birds and reptiles. It was, doubtless, from this common ancestor that bird and reptile inherit the habit of egg-laying. Some reptiles, our common lizard and viper for example, are viviparous—or more correctly, ovoviviparous; the egg is deposited but the young frees itself from the envelope either during the act of deposition or immediately afterwards. No birds are ovoviviparous, but there is great variation in the age and appearance of the young when hatched.

Take two familiar examples—the Robin and a duck—say a Teal, as we are dealing with wild and not domesticated species. The infant Robin remains within the egg for a fortnight, the Teal takes about double that time to reach hatching stage. What is the result? The baby Robin is blind, helpless, unformed when it breaks the shell; it is a big-headed weakling, a monstrosity, and shows very few characters that suggest Robin, and few indeed which are really avian. It is indeed little more than an embryo, and is entirely dependent upon the good offices of its parents. The little Teal, however, though it cannot be said to show much likeness to its parents, emerges as a perfect little duck; it can see, feed, run, and enjoy life as soon as its downy coat is dry. True, it is devoid of real feathers and its forelimbs are tiny hands rather than wings, but it has a full covering of soft, close down, and its little webbed feet, as attractive in their own way as the feet of human infants, are ready to paddle as soon as it leaves the egg. We shall see more of this engaging infant in a later chapter.

Embryology: The term Embryology is derived from a Greek word which means "growth within," for it is the growth within the egg shell that first demands attention when we wish to know something about the Infancy of birds. Embryology, though intensely interesting, is far too technical and difficult a science to explain in a popular book. Nevertheless, as we are anxious to trace the story of the bird from its very beginnings we must look at the inside as well as the outside of the shell.

The child who eats a boiled egg knows that when he has cracked the shell there is below it a second covering—a tough, parchment-like white skin. Sometimes when he knocks off the "top"—for eggs are generally placed in the egg-cup with the blunter end uppermost—he finds that there is a distinct chamber or space between the shell and this skin. This separation of shell and skin, however, is not noticeable in any other part of the egg; except at the top the two are in contact. The chamber is the air-chamber, and it grows larger the longer the egg is kept, for the shell of the egg is porous and some of its albuminous contents evaporate. Within the skin is the albuminous liquid that coagulates when the egg is boiled and is then known as the "white"; within the white again is the yellow yolk, and at one spot on that yolk is the future chick, the bird to be.

Probably most children have at one time spooned out some of the white and exclaimed: "What a funny little screw" or "twist," for at either end of the egg is a twisted bit or cord of albumen, harder than the rest. Sometimes the wise elders will tell the child to throw the nasty thing away, imagining that it is the future chicken and that the egg is not fresh! It is perfectly natural; part of every egg. The function of this thickened twist is not certain, but, as it is not attached to either shell or yolk, it cannot serve, as was at one time thought, to keep the yolk right side up. As a matter of fact the mother bird constantly stirs her eggs, but that is not to give every side of the yolk its turn; for nature arranges that whichever way the egg lies the yolk, floating in its albumen, shall roll over so that the embryo is next to the warm breast of the sitting bird.

Development during incubation, that is to say during the time that the mother bird is sitting, varies in time but follows certain regular rules. Changes are apparent at the end of the first day, but the subsequent changes are more rapid in a species that takes only two weeks to develop than in one that takes a month or more. If we followed an egg from day to day we should see first the notochord, the future vertebral column, and very quickly the one end thickens where the head will be.

In the domestic fowl, a bird that requires about three weeks for full development, the heart, centre of the future circulatory blood system, appears on the second day, and the opposite end of the notochord lengthens into what may at once be termed the tail. Then slowly, day after day, the embryo spreads its growing blood vessels round its food supply, the yolk, embracing it with its nourishment tappers. Other blood vessels extend to the shell, for they are to aid in breathing. Brain, eye, lungs and digestive organs show, and our embryonic bird reaches a typical vertebrate stage. It is now very much like the young, at a corresponding stage, of any other vertebrate animal, be it fish, reptile, or mammal. In the chick the embryo can be recognised as bird on about the sixth day, and a few days before it is to emerge it has taken in the whole of the remainder of the yolk, and has consumed most of the white. Now we see feathers appearing, and finally on that soft, undeveloped beak a hard lump, chalky in appearance, known as the egg-tooth, with which it breaks its way out of its prison.

Hatching: The egg-tooth is a hard and more or less pointed knob of lime which forms on the tip of the upper mandible of the beak of the now well-developed chick within the egg. With that strange instinct that teaches an unreasoning animal how to make use of the powers which nature has provided, the chick rubs the egg-tooth from side to side against the inner surface of the shell. After a time the shell gives way, and we say that it is chipping, and then in due course the top or lid of the shell is rubbed through and with a few convulsive struggles the infant emerges into the light of day. Some parent birds give gentle help in smashing the shell, but often the movements of the young accomplish the advent unaided.

Now we come back to the difference between the Robin and the Teal. The first belongs to a group that has been called by various names; the one first used being "altricial" young, from the Latin word *altrix*, a female nourisher. The explanation is that the robin, and other altricial birds, are, when first hatched, too feeble to feed themselves, and are so sparsely clad with down that if the mother bird did not warm them they would perish. Later the term "nidicolous" was applied to them, as they are the birds which remain or abide in the nest. The other group was called the "precocial" young, a word which explains itself; but that was altered to "nidifugous," as the young leave or fly from the nest at once.

A number of birds refuse to follow all the rules that were set down for these two groups, and it is soon clear that no real scientific classification is possible on these lines. For instance, as we shall see later, some of these nest-stickers, if we may call them that, are born with quite a quantity of warm down, whilst others, though naked at first, get their woolly covering very swiftly. The young Robin, blind like all of the group, is almost naked, but has a few immature true feathers showing, and at the tip of these wavy, soft, but sparse down. A few kinds, birds that nest in holes, never have any down at all, and among these is a bird which may be hatched in a hole or in the open,

MALE REED-BUNTING AT NEST.

according to the situation of the nest of the species on which the mother puts her nursing out, the familiar Cuckoo.

Precocial, or better still our word precocious, is a more descriptive name for the other type of nestling. Nidifugous birds are described as being independent of parental care, for they are born with open eyes and have this first down plumage to keep them warm. Granting that they might be able to find food for themselves at once, and that their coats are thick enough to keep them from severe chills, there are very few of them which are ready at once to cast aside parental care. Perhaps their mothers have spoiled them for so many generations that they have become degenerate, but the thoughtful, anxious mother bird broods her downy chicks, and where she does not actually give them food, she shows them where to find it.

The Great Crested Grebe is a typical precocious youngster, but even when it is half as big as its mother, it follows her about with such insistent demands for food that for the sake of peace she often catches fishes for it, and actually hands them over. She does not brood the little ones much in the nest, we shall see why later, but she lets them warm themselves on her back, providing them with a living nest between her upraised wings. Very baldly the two divisions are those that *must* be looked after when they are juvenile, and those which should not need it but *are* cared for. Such great authorities as Bonaparte and Newton differed as to where certain families of birds should be placed. Bonaparte considered the gulls, with eyes open at birth, were typical Altrices, but Newton places them with the Praecoces. Now young gulls are in no hurry to leave the nest, though they can stand very soon after they have got rid of the shell. We can, however, leave these questions for the system-

B

atist to settle, for what really interests us is how the young behave and how their parents treat them.

The down clothing is as a rule a first plumage, and it is shed when the true feathers grow. Baby hawks and owls look queer little objects when the down is half shed, and many passerine birds, the big group to which the Robin and Sparrow belong, keep traces of down on the top of the head when they are really quite respectably feathered infants. The true feathers come gradually, and they do not grow, except in a few species, from all parts of the body. There are naked places from which no feathers spring, but when the young bird is fully feathered all these bare patches are screened or covered by the neat way in which the perfect feathers lie.

There are some birds, however, which keep an additional short downy covering, warm underclothes we might call them, to keep the bare places warm and dry. Our little Teal gets a permanent down covering when it has shed its nestling down. The arrangement of these feather tracts and bare spaces is not the same on all birds, and there has been quite a study of the geography of the mapped out feather tracts.

Feathering and Moults: Birds are unique in the possession of feathers, though there is really relationship between feathers and hair, and even with nails and horns, for they are all alike modified scales or skin covering, a portion of the outer skeleton or framework of the animal. It is a little startling to realise that the sheaths of the beak and the scaly covering of the legs of birds are really part of this same outer covering, though their growth and development is quite distinct. The first feathers appear as little tufts protruding from a sheath. Feathers differ very much in structure and form, but a typical feather consists of a quill, which fits into a pit in the skin, a shaft, an after shaft, by no means always present, and a vane springing from the shaft. The vane is made up of a number of *barbs*, and these again are fitted with many *barbules*, or little barbs, roughly at right angles to the main barb. These barbules cross over one another, and interlock by a series of tiny hooks. If a feather be drawn through the finger and thumb—stroked the wrong way—the hooks come unhooked, but by a careful manipulation they can be replaced and the feather look as perfect and tidy as ever.

In all birds that fly, the big flight feathers are of the greatest importance, for though there are many creatures that are capable of flight or aerial locomotion — insects, flying fish, bats, and inanimate mechanical structures such as aeroplanes,—there is nothing to equal the mechanism of the feather-flight. The first feathers to grow to any size are the big flight feathers, but the tail sprouts about the same time, but takes much longer to attain its full dimensions. It does not matter how thick and complete the downy covering of the young bird, these important feathers come quickly, but they are not permanent. Feathers, as we can see, are very neat and complicated structures, but they are frail, and suffer severely from wear and tear; so when they have become worn and are not fit for full service they are shed and replaced, the change being known as the Moult. There is as a rule only one complete moult in the year in mature birds, but, as we shall see later, there are very distinct changes which are more or less of the nature of a moult. In many birds the spring change, when the feathers look so much cleaner and brighter than during winter, is caused by the shedding of portions of the feathers, the tips and edges. Patches of self colour, without obscuring rims or end markings, are thus obtained, and the bird looks as if it had grown a completely new set of feathers.

The dress which is first attained by the young is not worn

for long.   In the Robin, the bird we have taken as an example, the sooty down of the nestling is followed by a juvenile plumage which is for the most part shed during the summer, but the flight and tail feathers, and indeed many of the larger wing feathers are retained.

The different sexes of birds cannot, as a rule, be told in the juvenile dress, but when the next summer or autumn moult is accomplished the sex markings, in those species that have a male and female plumage, can almost invariably be detected.   Some birds attain a mature dress very quickly, others take a long time; we shall see more of this in a later chapter.

NIGHTINGALE.

CHAPTER II

Nests

THE egg is the first stage of the young bird, but, to thoroughly understand the egg, something must be said about the receptacle in which it is placed, for in many cases the situation of the nest and its formation has bearing upon the colour and shape of the egg, as well as upon the number of eggs which are laid at one time.

The Nest is the bird's home, but, except in a very few instances, it is a temporary home; indeed it is nothing more than a nursery. The Wren is one of very few birds which uses its nest after the young have flown, and it appears that when the Wren needs a winter dormitory it is a nest, and not necessarily its own nest, that it uses. Also any hole, if warm enough, will serve just as well; it is the shelter from the storm, not the nest that the bird demands. Most nests are deserted by old and young alike so soon as the babes are able to leave them; the nest may be built so well that it will survive the winter, but it is not wanted again. It is true that there are birds that will occupy an old nest, but when this happens it is usually that of some other species, and in most cases the old nest simply serves as a convenient platform on which to build a superstructure.

As examples of birds which often like to save themselves the trouble of foundation building we have the Sparrow-Hawk, and the Tawny and Long-eared Owls. I have known the Tawny to sit in the nest of the Carrion-Crow, and as this nest was well lined I have strong suspicion that the Owl suggested to the Crow

13

that the nest was just what it wanted. The Crow may have objected, but the Tawny Owl can by puffing out its plumage, snapping its bill, and, in fact, making grimaces, look very ferocious, and the Carrion-Crow is not gifted with great courage, however cunning it may be.

In other cases that I have come across, one bird has built a nest upon or within the remnants of the old discarded nest of another species. The big mud cup which often holds together the remnants of last year's nest of a Song-Thrush, will accommodate the new nest of a Pied Wagtail or Spotted Flycatcher, and occasionally the Wren finds an old nest convenient to build upon. The same nesting hole may be used year after year—the Tits do this constantly, but a new nest is built, or at any rate new lining carried into the hole.

In spite of the fact that the nursery is only required for a short time, a few weeks in the spring, it is often so firmly constructed that more than a winter's storms fail to destroy it. The mud lining of the nest of the Song-Thrush, just referred to, will remain after all the outer foundation has decayed, and a leafless hedgerow is an exposed situation. The masses of sticks and turf interwoven and moulded together by the Rook and Carrion-Crow will stand the swing of the storm-tossed tree, and be ready for repair or destruction when the birds decide that it is time to be house-building once more.

There is, however, immense variation in nests, and many birds build very slight structures; a few make no nest at all. The rock auks, Guillemot and Razorbill, and the Nightjar and Norfolk Plover or Stone-Curlew lay the egg or eggs on bare rock or ground. Between these no nest builders and those which construct a durable and elaborate house for eggs and young is an immense variety of styles of architecture and site. As to

Woodcock.

whether the ancestral bird built no nest or an elaborate one, or whether it nested in a tree or on the ground; these are not matters which greatly concern us here; what we do want to see is what the birds we know around us accomplish; the arguments about primitive habits are interesting, but they are arguments and nothing more. We cannot with certainty decide what the reptile-like birds did and why they did it.

As species, birds follow certain ancestral rules in nest construction, but birds are as variable as men, and just as some men like an elegant house in some particular style, whilst others are content with anything so long as it is dry and cosy, so we find individuality amongst birds of the same species. Starting from the simple and working up to the elaborate, we find a very curious difference in the Terns. Two species of Tern, the Common and the Arctic may often be found in the same colony, the situation of which may be a rocky islet or a stretch of sandy dunes. The two birds are so much alike that it is almost impossible to tell them when they are on the wing, and, if we cannot see their bills, not always easy when they are at rest.

The Arctic, more of a rock frequenter than the Common, often makes no nest at all, but places its two or three eggs on the bare rock; occasionally it makes a fair sized nest, but the commonest habit is to arrange a few grass bents or scraps of herbage round the eggs, a decorative border rather than a nest. Bleached bones of other birds or of rabbits are sometimes collected and placed round the eggs. The Common Tern varies even more than the Arctic, for at times she will do nothing more than scoop a saucer-shaped hollow in the sand, but other nests are well lined and have a considerable quantity of nesting material. The Golden Plover, a moorland species, makes use of the surrounding vegetation, for a hollow in ling, crowberry or bilberry, is a ready-made nest: the living vegetation around forms stout walls and effective screens.   The Redshank, another wader, shows great variation in taste, for, like the Common Sandpiper, it will at times build a very slight structure in the open, and at other times carefully conceal its home.   This bird has a frequent habit of constructing a tent or tunnel over the actual nest by drawing together and interweaving the blades or flower stems of the long marsh grasses.

As already stated the Guillemot and Razorbill make no attempt at a nest; the large single egg is deposited on a rocky ledge of some steep cliff, or, in exceptional places, on the flat top of high rocks.   On those strange craggy islets of the Farnes, known as the Pinnacles, the Guillemots crowd together in such dense masses that it seems impossible that any bird can recognise its own egg or young; there is no division between the territory of each pair.   The quaint Puffin is another auk, and it too lays a single egg, but it has altered its methods, for there is a suggestion that it once laid in the open, and now nests in a burrow.   These holes, often made by rabbits, often excavated by the bird itself, vary greatly in length or depth; at times the bird lays under an overhanging rock or in a crevice.   Yet where the egg is laid there is a distinct attempt at a nest, a hollow chamber, usually a little bigger than the tunnel, and a hollow scooped in the floor; in this primitive nest the bird places a few soft weeds or grasses, making a lining.   The Razorbill in its habits comes half way between the Guillemot and the Puffin, for though it does not make any nest, it prefers to find a sheltered ledge to one which is entirely exposed.   It will sit, crouching prone, in some longitudinal crack in the rock face, whereas the Guillemot incubates in an upright position and demands head-room.

PUFFINS.

One would imagine that birds which nested in tunnels would require very little bedding, but another usurper of the rabbit's burrow, the Sheld-duck, thinks otherwise, for during incubation it plucks out its own soft, warm down and arranges it round the eggs. Thus by the time that incubation is well advanced there is a wonderfully cosy nest, the lining made entirely of down, for the young to find around them when they emerge from the shell. This self sacrificial method, for surely the mother misses the comfort of inner plumage, is common amongst ducks, and man exploits the unfortunate female Eiders for the sake of his own comfort. The best down quilts are filled with Eider down, for it is warmer, lighter, and more elastic than that of other ducks; the grey down of the Sheld-duck is not only warm but very beautiful, and if it could be obtained in large quantities would probably find a ready market.

The nests of most Gulls are large and untidy, a litter of turf, straw, grass and weed. Nor are they very clean, although the bird's plumage looks so spotless. Pellets of undigested food, fragments of fishy matter, and litter of all kinds are left in the nest and trampled into a mess by the webbed feet of parents and chicks; the nests too are usually placed on the flat, or at any rate on a wide and firm base. The dainty Kittiwake, a bird whose undeveloped hind toe puts it in a different genus from most gulls, differs as much in nesting habits as in feet. The Kittiwake plays for safety, like the Guillemot, for she builds on the ledges, and often on a very much narrower ledge than the auks demand. A nest built on a ledge is liable to be swept off by strong winds, or overturned by the movements of its occupants, but the Kittiwake is an accomplished plasterer, and constructs a nest that will stick. It is not a very large nest, for the accommodation is limited, but made of clay, mud, wet seaweed and grass, well paddled together by active webbed feet, it becomes as solid as cement.

The Red-legged Partridge, the Pheasant, and many other game-birds, trust more to the security provided by dense vegetation than to the structure of the nest. It is true that some effort is made to build, but this consists in the Partridge at any rate, in lining a hollow in the hedgerow with grass and dead leaves. Occasionally, however, the bird evinces a desire to build in an elevated position, and will lay its eggs on the top of a haystack. The Pheasant often almost smothers itself and its eggs in dead leaves, and another bird that is fond of snuggling its eggs in leaves, especially those of the oak, is the secretive Woodcock.

The Rails make fairly large nests, but they differ from one another in habits, and the nests are adapted to the environment. Thus the Corncrake, a bird of dry surroundings, builds a large grass nest, well hidden in long sedges or grasses, and often bends the blades over to provide a screen rather than a shelter from weather. The Moor-hen may select a thick tuft of rushes, and balance her flat blade-made nest upon them, or she may take advantage of a half submerged snag or bush to give foundation for a well constructed saucer that will hold together in the way that a nest should. The overhanging branches of alders or other waterside trees make a platform for some nests, and I have found them in thick evergreens, in fir trees, and at a considerable distance from water and often many feet above the ground.

The Coot's nest is in reeds if reeds are available, and is made of reeds, sedges, or reed-mace blades; it is in rather than on the water, for the base either lies on the litter of broken stems or if the water is shallow enough starts from the bottom. The Coot is, however, alive to the fact that the level of water varies, and she will add more and more material so as to raise the whole nest when there is a rainy spell. Then when the water recedes again we understand why some nests look like haystacks, very conspicuous objects in the reed-bed. The Water-rail is a shyer, more retiring bird than any of those mentioned, and her nest is in the deepest, most treacherous part of the marsh. It is necessary that it should not get waterlogged with the weight of the family, so when she starts building she forms a raft or platform of broken stems, stout enough to hold the flat structure above, even when the ground is little but liquid ooze.

If we next consider the birds which, in most modern schemes of classification, are placed between the game-birds and the rails we have the Pigeons, and here we find an entirely different type of nest, though all pigeons are not alike in method. The Ring-dove or Wood-Pigeon, and the smaller Turtle-dove, apparently throw together a few sticks haphazard, for the platform is so frail that the eggs are often visible from below. But appearances are deceptive, for these simple twigs are so cleverly interwoven through the branches that support them, and with one another, that the nest will often survive until the following summer. The Rock-dove either nests in a deep crack in rock or in a cave; she likes a roof over her head, however much the sea may crash and moan in the darkness below her; on her nesting ledge she collects a sparse lining of feathers, seaweed and grass. The Stock-dove also desires shelter, but seldom troubles with any lining. The situations she selects are holes in trees, where there is a ready lining of rotten wood and tinder, rabbit burrows, holes in ruins or in rocks, the deserted nest of some other bird or a disused squirrel drey.

The Grebes go a stage further than the Water-rail and Coot, for though they delight in a watery surrounding they prefer deep to shallow water; their nests usually float but are held in position by the stems of the aquatic plants. They rise and fall on their anchorage with the variation of height of the water. These floating nests are mostly composed of truly aquatic plants, water weeds, which the old birds bring up from below the surface. Naturally they are more than moist, they are sodden.

The wet bed gradually ferments and produces a considerable amount of heat, but whether the bird has any instinctive desire to utilise this heat for incubation is uncertain; the idea has originated from the fact that the nests are warm, and that the bird covers its eggs when it leaves them. But the act of covering is protective, and the instinct for protection is more easily evolved than any knowledge of physics. The effect of this egg covering habit and its methods we shall deal with in later chapters.

Returning to the big group known as the Wading Birds, whose habits we have barely touched upon, we find the same variation in nest development, though as a rule the nests themselves are little more than hollows. The Oyster-catcher selects various situations for its nest, and individual Oyster-catchers exhibit a diversity of taste in the matter of decoration. A flat spot on sandy dunes or on the beach, a hollow between rocks on a stack, the shingle beach of a Scottish loch or river, the edge of a cliff, or the middle of a grass field are all positions in which I have personally found the nest. Sometimes there is no lining whatever to the neatly scraped hollow, sometimes a surround of intertwisted bents, but a lining of vegetation is often provided; seaweed is used for bedding in some nests, but in others the lining is of a more unyielding nature—beach pebbles, marine shells and, like the Arctic Tern, bones bleached by exposure. That selection of decoration is used, is proved by

PIED FLYCATCHER.

Drawn from an unusual nest at Buttermere ; the eggs,
and, later, the young birds were visible and could be
handled.

the fact that one lining was entirely composed of limpets, but in another nest the banded shells of the land mollusc, *Helix nemoralis*, had been used, and nothing else.

The slight nests of Lapwing and Golden Plover have been mentioned, and many other waders, such as the Ringed Plover and Curlew, pay little attention to structure or decoration, but on the other hand the Green Sandpiper, though it is not proved to be a species which has nested in Britain, varies from all other British sandpipers in its arboreal habits. It does not actually make a nest in a tree, but uses as a platform for its eggs an old nest or a squirrel drey. It may be that this habit has been overlooked, and that Green Sandpipers have nested in Britain without being discovered.

Amongst the Herons we find the Bittern making a large nest of reeds or other plants in the middle of wet beds of aquatic vegetation, and like the Water-rail, it breaks down the stems so as to give a foundation on oozy ground; the Heron on the other hand, though it occasionally nests on rocks, is as a rule an arboreal species, and its massive nests, several in one tree at times, remind us of rookeries.

The nests of Cormorant, Shag and Gannet, all cliff breeders but in no ways related to gulls, are all large, and are mainly composed of seaweed, though the Gannet often adds great masses of turf or anything that it can drag from the cliff top with its powerful beak. It also likes decoration and has quaint tastes, for candle ends, a parasol, much dirty paper, and golf balls have been found in the nests. The Vultures, none of which nest in England, show the same delight in turning their nests into marine stores, and the fouler the rags, paper, or bits of rope that they can discover the more they seem to appreciate them. Cormorants occasionally build bulky nests in trees, but the structure must be more cleverly interwoven than the wet seaweed heap which is usually accumulated.

A similar delight in extraordinary decoration is shown by many of the raptorial birds. "When the Kite builds, look to lesser linen," was the warning of Autolycus, for this bird used to be a thief of anything in the rag line, and still, where it is allowed to build, adds what it can steal. The Golden Eagle, which builds a massive nest, frequently adds to the walls or lining some freshly picked branches or sprigs with fresh green leaves. It apparently has an æsthetic taste. The situations in which the hawks and falcons nest determine the size and quality of the nests, for the Merlin, which almost invariably nests on the ground, is satisfied with a mere hollow in the turf. I have seen the nest in a tree, but it was in that of a Carrion-Crow. The Kestrel may use an arboreal site or a rocky ledge, but the nest in the tree was originally built by some other bird; she merely makes use of the old foundation. One of the most beautiful and cosy Kestrel's nests that I have ever seen was no nest at all; the bird had merely hollowed out the top of a great clump of thrift, which, when the ruddy eggs were in the nest, was in full flower; the bird was sitting in its own garden.

The Osprey, a big fish hawk, is another bird that uses different situations, building a bulky nest in either a tree or on the top of some rock or ruined building. It is, like the nest of the Kite, a rubbish heap, and Mr Bahr tells how in one nest in America he found the wheel of a child's mail-cart, numerous corks, and the skeleton of a bird. If the Merlin and Kestrel are too lazy to make nests, the Sparrow-Hawk is not, for her big nest, usually of fir twigs, is very well made. She is one of the few birds which will return to the actual nest she has used before, but she very carefully mends and improves it, adding fresh material, so that it grows to be a conspicuous object, and would be very much more noticeable were it not frequently in a non-deciduous conifer.

The Owls are not nest builders, though the eggs of Tawny, Long-eared Owls or other species may be in nests; they make use of what they can find, and seldom if ever add lining. Even the Short-eared Owl, which habitually nests on the ground, seldom troubles to provide any bedding for the eggs. The Barn-Owl frequently lays its eggs upon a soft lining, but this is not fetched from a distance; it consists entirely of the dry pellets or "plugs" which the bird throws up at intervals. These pellets are composed of the fur, feather, and broken bones of the creatures upon which it has preyed; they are the undigestible portions of its food which it rejects. As they are mainly composed of fur they dry into a thickly felted mass, and must be quite a comfortable bed for the youngsters. The nest of the Kingfisher also consists of "cast up" matter, but this is entirely composed of fish bones and scales; the Kingfisher throws up the refuse which it cannot digest in its bedroom; it is not really a nest. The nest chamber, where the bones accumulate, is at the end of a deep tunnel, which is skilfully bored so that the mouth is lower than the chamber, and all liquid runs down the slope to the doorway.

The bird-nest soup which is occasionally imported from the east, and which the Chinese consume with avidity, is usually described as being manufactured from the nests of Swallows, but this is not so, the bird is a Swift. Our own Swift makes a nest which, if cleaner, would be edible, for a few straws and other rubbish are glued together in a mass of salivary secretion, which rapidly hardens, and it is this hardened jelly which the

Chinese boil into soup. The Woodpeckers bore the nesting holes in decayed or soft-wooded trees, but they make no real nest, for the chips and wood-dust in the hollow provide a soft enough lining for the eggs.

The Passerine birds are the best nest builders, and though many of them utilise hollows for nesting chambers, there is in practically every case a nest neatly fitted in, as well as a lining. These are the more highly developed or more specialised birds; it is not surprising that their architectural skill surpasses that of more primitive types.

The typical passerine nest is a deep saucer, a neatly woven structure of grass, stems, roots or sticks, intertwisted so skilfully that we can pick the whole up without it coming to pieces. Within this outer shell is the lining, which often consists of entirely different materials from the outer covering; these may be finer stems or rootlets, hair (horse-hair is freely used), feathers or wool. In some, the nests of Song-Thrush, Blackbird and Ring-Ousel for instance, there is what we term a mud lining but really is a felted cement, for in the material of which it is made is introduced a quantity of wood chips, short lengths of straw, and bits of grass stem. The Thrush is satisfied with this, but the Blackbird and Ring-Ousel add an inner grass lining. An interesting point to notice in the nest of this moorland Blackbird is that the grasses of which the outer nest is constructed are hard and stiff, typical hill kinds, and the ends if originally tucked in by the builder spring out again; the nest has stiff stems sticking out from it at all angles; the softer more brittle material which the lowland bird uses makes a neater but no better nest.

These open nests may be in hedgerows, in bushes, well hidden and protected by prickles like that of the Dartford Warbler, in trees, on the ground, as those of Larks and Pipits, in hollows,

Yellow-Hammers.

as Redstart, Robin, Pied Flycatcher, or in more unusual situations. The Robin, for instance, though it builds an open nest, desires a shelter, and anything that will keep off the rain suits it. An old kettle, a discarded boot, a flower pot on its side, an ancient straw hat, are amongst the quaint situations selected by this versatile bird.

Amongst the Crows the open nest is general, but the situation varies, for though the Raven, Crow, and Rook select open sites, the Jackdaw and Chough build in holes in rocks or ruined buildings. Nevertheless, the Daw is reverting to the open situation, and I have examined many open nests built in trees, resembling the nests of the Rook. These corvine nests are well made, strengthened with masses of turf, to give foundation amongst their stick platforms. Many of them are neatly lined with wool, providing a very warm cradle for the young. One of the crows, however, the Magpie, adds a covering, a well built dome of sticks, often prickly, above the main structure. It is doubtful if this is for shelter, but it certainly is a protection. These big domed nests are usually in tall trees, but occasionally in bushes or hedgerows, and where there are no trees, as in certain coast localities, the bird will nest upon the ground. In one of these cliff-nests on the ground the Magpie had built no actual covering—but the sticks were arranged in front of the nest cup—the rock was behind—so as to provide a stout hedge to keep away enemies. The cup of the Jackdaw's nest is sometimes very small compared with the huge quantity of sticks collected. One nest I remember was built close to the window slit in a tower staircase. The bird had dropped its sticks into this likely-looking hole, but the more it put in the more they slipped down on to lower stairs, so that in the end the actual nest was a pyramid of sticks, which would have filled several

c

barrows, resting on five or six steps; at the top of the cone was the nest cup.

Covered or partially covered nests are an advance on the open nest. The leaf-warblers—Willow-Wren, Chiffchaff and Wood-Wren—make neat semi-domed nests, placed as a rule on or near the ground. Kingsley declares, in "*Juventus Mundi*," that they build

"Not nests but houses,
Like the bumble-bees and mousies."

The dome of the Wren's nest is as a rule more complete, but as the bird frequently builds in a ready made hollow, it is not always lined at the top and back. One of the most interesting Wren's nests that I have come across was built under the wing of a dead Sparrow-Hawk that was hanging on a keeper's gibbet. Surely that was making use of a defeated enemy! Perhaps the most beautifully felted and perfect domed nest is that of the Long-tailed Titmouse. This nest is often in a hedge, and its outer covering studded with bits of lichen; the effect of this, though whether by intention or not I do not care to say, is to make the nest inconspicuous, for the light patches are not easily distinguishable from the light penetrating between the twigs. This nest is lined with feathers, often large feathers of Pheasants or Domestic Poultry, and an immense number are packed in; it is difficult to understand how there is room for all the " Bottle-tit's " numerous family, but somehow they do find room.

The domed nest of the Dipper is in many ways the most interesting of all the British nests, for it approaches in construction the wonderful mud nest of the South American Oven-bird. Externally the Dipper's home looks like a very large edition of the nest of the Wren. It is fitted into a hollow in

DIPPER.

some rocky bank of a stream, in the masonry of a bridge, or under a bank, and often is actually behind a waterfall. When built of moss it is kept green and fresh by the falling or splashing water, but in a dry situation it is composed of dead grasses. But this big nest, very large in proportion to the size of its owners, is really double, for the nest contains a nest. The upper lip of the mossy outer nest overlaps the lower, and thus the water cannot penetrate, and the entrance is in the lower half of the ball or ovoid. Within is the true nest, warm and dry, nearly as large as that of a Thrush, and comfortably lined with dry leaves of beech, oak or other trees.

The nest material used by passerine birds varies greatly, for amongst birds so closely related as the various finches, we find the nest of the Bullfinch loosely made of rootlets, that of the Hawfinch on a foundation of small twigs, and the carefully hidden nest of the Chaffinch an example of close felting—moss, lichens, fine grass and wool welded together so that a protectively coloured and waterproof cup is formed.

Other interesting nests are those of the Nightingale, built on or very close to the ground, and often entirely composed of oak leaves held together by grass, and of the Creeper, packed tightly in behind loose bark, and in consequence oval instead of round. The deep nest of the Reed-Warbler is suspended to two or three reed stems which grow through the rim; when the wind swings the pliant reeds the eggs or young within are merely rocked; the height of the wall protects them from being thrown out. The rarer Marsh-Warbler has a similar nest, not quite so deep, but it is attached to its supports by what Warde Fowler aptly termed "basket handles."

Three other nests must be noticed before the chapter closes, those of our three Swallows. The normal nest of the Swallow is a shallow mud saucer lined with feathers and grass. When it is placed against a beam and not on one, it is a half saucer.

The House-Martin, the swallow that builds under our eaves, makes a deeper nest, more of a half cup than saucer, and as it is always placed immediately below some shelter it is supported by attachment to the roof. It is built of mud, fetched by the bird in the form of moist pellets, and these are added in successive layers, and cake as they dry. In dry summers the birds are forced to travel long distances for plaster. I have seen large numbers gathered round the temporary puddle supplied by a watering-cart, and on the parched chalk downs House-Martins journey for miles to visit the edges of the few ponds. The third swallow, the Sand-Martin, burrows in sandy banks and places a few feathers and scraps of grass in the nest chamber.

CHAPTER III

Concerning Eggs

Every schoolboy knows the fascination of the bird's egg, and most budding naturalists begin by collecting eggs. Fortunately for birds the craze does not last long, and in most cases egg-collecting is forgotten before manhood is reached. There are, however, many grown-up egg-collectors, and though some make use of their collections for purposes of study, the majority, unfortunately, merely accumulate specimens. The egg has much to teach, and we have much to learn, but the sooner we realise that we can learn without destroying the better; the study of the egg can be accomplished without any "specimens." The egg in its natural setting, the nest, is the best teacher.

If, however, we look at a collection of eggs there are a number of points about it which will at once strike us. Difference in size will be most noticeable, but there is also great diversity of shape, and the variation in colour, even of eggs of the same species of bird, is very marked. There must be some reason for this, and as mentioned in the previous chapters two explanations may be expected, first—whether the bird is hatched early or late in its life within the egg, and secondly, in what kind of situation the nest is built. The eggs of precocious birds are very much larger in proportion to the size of the parent than those of the altricial species, the ones which are helpless for a long time before they leave the nest. But even here there is great variation, for closely allied species have eggs which differ

29

in this respect. The egg of the Guillemot is distinctly larger in proportion to the size of the bird than that of the Puffin for instance. The egg of the Cuckoo is very small, and we can easily see that this is an advantage, for if the Cuckoo's egg was large the foster parents might object to its presence in the nest. Abnormally large eggs and also dwarfed ones may be found in clutches where the others are normal, but exceptional variation of this kind occurs with all animals. Size alone is not a sufficiently distinct character for the identification of a Cuckoo's egg.

The shape of eggs is important in certain species, but the rules that are supposed to apply do not always work. The typical shape of an egg is Ovoid, a word that means egg-shaped. An ovoid is not quite an ellipse, one end is a little blunter than the other. The eggs of some of the ducks are nearly elliptical, but the eggs of most wading birds, the Redshank and Lapwing for example, are more pointed at the lower end, or south pole, than at the other; these eggs are termed Pyriform or pear-shaped. The eggs of the Long-eared Owl, and of the King-fisher are examples of round eggs, whilst those of the Swift and of the Great Crested Grebe are decidedly elongated.

No explanation of some of these shapes has been discovered, but there is apparent advantage in others. It is affirmed that the large pyriform egg of the Guillemot, which is placed without any protection on a bare ledge, turns on its widest part in the wind, swings round, in fact, like a weather-cock, and does not roll off the ledge. The egg of the Razorbill, being as a rule in a sheltered crack, does not require this shape, and is distinctly more ovoid. This is a very pretty theory, but has anyone ever seen the egg behaving in this manner? I doubt it. A much more reasonable explanation of the pyriform shape is that eggs

MEADOW-PIPIT.

arranged with the pointed ends inwards take up less room in a nest than if they are placed haphazard. Naturally this does not apply to the single egg of the Guillemot, but it certainly does to the eggs of waders, for very little experience of this family proves that the eggs are as a rule arranged in this manner in the nest. Four may be taken as the typical clutch of the typical wader, and in most cases the four have their ends pointing inwards. It is wonderful what a large amount of room is required for the exceptional five egg clutches of Lapwings; the nest hollow looks overcrowded. In most birds with ovoid or rounded eggs there is no regularity in the arrangement of the clutch, and as they are turned and shifted by the parent from time to time it would be difficult to keep them in order.

The most interesting variation in eggs is in their colour, but the theories which have been put forward to explain colour have so many exceptions to the rules that they must be accepted with caution. One thing is certain, eggs cannot protect themselves by escaping from enemies, and as species constantly wars against species, the evolution due to stress of circumstances tends to protect the helpless by one method or another. Colour is one of the chief protective forces; protective coloration is a most important asset for the bird, whether that protection is shown in the egg, the nest, or the plumage of young or mature bird. The primitive egg was almost certainly colourless, as are reptilian eggs to-day; colour is a development mainly due to the necessity of hiding the egg from the eyes of egg-eaters.

It is, of course, true that there are many white eggs to-day, but by one method or another these white eggs gain protection. The simplest method is, without doubt, concealment in the nest, and this is secured by the site. The eggs are deposited in a hole, a cave, or other dark situation. As examples of white eggs which are in covered nests, covered that is by the surroundings, we have in Britain very few amongst the passerine birds, for in them colour is as a rule well developed. The Sand-Martin has white eggs and they are well hidden in the burrows. The nest itself, rather than its situation, protects the eggs of the House-Martin and the Dipper. Amongst picarian birds there are more examples, for all the white eggs of Woodpeckers are in holes, as are those of the Kingfisher, Swift and Wryneck.

The Owls, especially the Barn and Little Owl, usually nest in dark places, though exposed situations are not unknown, and the Manx Shearwater, Puffin and Petrels also conceal the white eggs underground.

Many attempts have been made to prove, mainly following the theories of colour protection put forward by Wallace, that birds of bright plumage, especially where the female is as brilliant as the male, select dark situations. This applies to the Kingfisher, to the Woodpeckers in a lesser degree, and notice-ably to so remarkable a bird as the showy Bee-eater. But the pale brown Sand-Martin and the sooty Swift cannot be called showy, and their sexes are alike.

Many of the eggs of our smaller birds have white grounds, and though they are sparsely spotted or mottled with brown, red or lavender, they are white enough to be conspicuous; these in most cases are concealed. The Swallow, though it builds an open nest, usually places it well out of sight in the gloom of a barn or other outbuilding; the Titmice nest in holes, the Creeper finds a screen of loose bark, the Wren with its covered nest hides its often nearly white eggs. Even the Robin, whose eggs may be ruddy, protects them by the artificial surroundings when it cannot find a suitable natural hollow. The Nuthatch, which has many habits suggestive of the woodpeckers, to which it is in no way related, shares with them the hole-method of shielding its speckled white eggs.

The eggs of the Starling, very pale blue, are undoubtedly conspicuous, and they are always in some well sheltered hole in tree or building; indeed the cute, go-ahead "Shepster" does not content itself with imitating the methods of the Woodpeckers, but saves itself the trouble of excavating or searching for similar hollows in trees by evicting the rightful owners.

Amongst the Crows we find great variation in the amount of colour, but two of them, the Chough and Jackdaw, prefer sheltered situations, and these have the palest eggs of the group. Those with exposed nests, such as the Raven, Carrion and Hoodie Crow, have remarkably protectively coloured eggs, so thickly smeared and blotched with green that the eye of an egg robbing bird passing above the nests might easily miss them. Perhaps these corvids have learnt by personal experience, for they are the worst offenders in the matter of egg filching, and no doubt do not trust their nearest relatives. "Dog does not eat dog," and "honour amongst thieves" are proverbial sayings, but lack foundation, for the building Rook has to keep a close watch on its half finished nest or it may find the sticks it has laboriously gathered woven into its neighbour's domicile. The Daw, as has been stated, shows a desire to use an open nest; will the eggs darken in time? We shall see, if the habit grows and we live long enough to appreciate evolutionary changes. The Jay has paler, but still well protected greenish eggs, and it builds in an open nest, and though the eggs of the Magpie are sometimes pale and sometimes well coloured the dome of sticks above them not only shelters them from sight, but keeps marauders at a safe distance.

A very pale egg is that of the White-tailed Eagle, now,

unfortunately, no longer a British nesting bird ; the nest is open, the eggs are conspicuous, but the bird is powerful and the egg-robber dare not take liberties. The eggs of Harriers are white, tinged with blue, and sometimes slightly spotted ; they are in nests on the marsh, or in what might be considered open places, but undoubtedly they get a measure of protection from the screening vegetation around, and moral protection from the power of their owners. Those of another marsh nester, the Bittern, are self coloured, but their browns are in harmony with the colour of the reed-stems and other plants of which the big nest is made, and the withered vegetation around it. The Heron is a relative of the Bittern that builds in trees, and its eggs are blue. The egg is large and no doubt tasty, and there is a constant feud between Rooks and Herons, but though Rooks will inspect the temptations from above they will not venture to steal if there are any Herons on guard, and the fact that the Heron is a sociable species, nesting in a colony, gives the robbers few opportunities of finding the nests without some sentinels at hand.

Other powerful birds nesting in colonies whose eggs are white or tinged are the Cormorant, Shag and Gannet ; human robbers are the worst foes of these birds, and the situations of the cliff nests render human raids difficult.

The eggs of Pigeons are conspicuously white, but here there is another protection. The nests of Ring-dove and Turtle are so loosely constructed that it is possible that the light penetrating between the sticks makes it difficult to see from above whether there are or are not eggs in the nest. This theory does not commend itself to the critical mind, for the ground below—the background of an aerial picture—will be dark. Yet it is reasonable to argue that the eggs cannot suffer much, for the clutch

YOUNG CARRION-CROWS.

is small, a couple, no more. If there was considerable drain on the species from egg destruction, the species would die out. Rock- and Stock-doves nest in sheltered situations.

Although the eggs of Ducks are often tinted with cream, blue or green, they are light and noticeable on the ground, and of these, in England at any rate, the Sheld-duck is the only one that habitually uses a covered site. It is true that some ducks, the Mallard for instance, will cover the eggs when they leave them, and that they get a certain amount of protection from the down which accumulates round them during incubation, but the greatest security is from the sitting bird. In most of the ducks the female is much milder in her garments than the male, and she does all the incubating. She is a close sitter, and so long as she remains quietly sitting on the eggs the chance that the nest will be overlooked is good. In the Sheld-duck both sexes are brightly coloured, so that the burrow is a distinct advantage.

Female protective colour also screens the eggs, brown or olive, of Pheasant and Partridge, and these, too, may be covered by the bird when she leaves them for a time. But the most expert egg coverers are the Grebes; with them the act of hiding the eggs is more than instinctive, it is practically reflex. If the nest of Great Crested Grebe or Dabchick be approached, the sitting bird will rise and by two or three hurried pecks pull some of the nesting material over the eggs before she slips away. The nest with its full clutch looks like nothing more interesting than an accumulation of litter. This habit of covering the eggs with wet weed serves another purpose, for the texture of the outer covering of the shell is chalky and absorbent; the green and brown juices of rotting vegetation soon stain the eggs so that they are less easy to see than when they were freshly laid.

Passing on to coloured eggs we would repeat the statement that it is probable that primitive eggs were white and that colour is a later development, largely evolved for purposes of protection, but subject to that great law of Variation which is the root of all evolutionary advance or change. Colour may be deeply embedded in the shell, when it is termed underlying, or it may be more on the surface; it may be what is known in textile trades as "fast," that is, not easily obliterated, or "loose" when it will wash or wear off. A changed habit may alter coloration, and it does not follow that the eggs will only darken. Thus we have the white eggs of the Puffin, Manx Shearwater and Storm and Leach's Petrels, all of which are concealed in burrows or underground, on which there are usually faint underlying markings. Almost certainly the underground habit is not original in these birds, and it looks as if the eggs were losing colour or markings through the disuse of these protective aids. The zone of pale grey marks round the thicker end of the Puffin's egg, and the fine speckles on those of the smaller Petrels are very good examples of degeneration through disuse.

Though the eggs of finches—Chaffinch, Redpoll, Crossbill, for example—are tastefully mottled or spotted, there is nothing about them to suggest value from the protective point of view; they show hereditary specific characters which so far we cannot explain. In the large genus *Emberiza*, the Buntings, of which the Reed-Bunting is a good example, there are a few or many irregular lines or "scribbles" in addition to the ordinary mottles and washes, from which the Yellow-hammer gets a local name "scribbling lark." One old man assured me that there was a cryptic message on the eggs, an occult threat against egg robbers; evidently a similar myth to the one which in Scotland associates

Merlin.

the bird with the Devil. In most finches the position of the nest, screened by the surrounding foliage, secures protection. Ground-nesting Larks, however, and also Pipits, have heavily coloured eggs, by no means conspicuous where there is any bare soil, or where the sheltering grasses produce gloom. Wagtails' eggs are paler in ground tint but are profusely speckled.

The tiny eggs of the Goldcrest are finely marked, but are light enough to be seen in the nest were it not for its clever position, for it is slung, a dainty hammock, beneath the dark branch of a fir; neither nest nor eggs are visible from above. The eggs of Shrikes are beautifully marked, with varying ground wash and a zone of colour round the broadest part; the nest is well hidden in a thick bush or hedge.

The Warblers which nest in covered nests have lighter, more easily seen eggs than the open nest species; indeed some of the varied eggs of Blackcap and Garden-Warbler are so profusely mottled that they are well hidden when in the nest, however conspicuous they may look in a cabinet. It is not possible to learn anything about the colour values of eggs unless we see them in their proper setting—the nest.

The various Thrushes present some interesting problems, for the closely speckled eggs of Blackbird and Ring-Ousel are much better protected than those of Mistle- and Song-Thrush. Every boy knows that the black spotted, blue eggs of the last bird are easier to find than those of any other birds, but in spite of the fact that the Thrush builds a large conspicuous nest in a roadside hedge, often before there are screening leaves, and that the nest is frequently robbed, there is no noticeable diminution in the Song-Thrush population. It is true that the Mistle-Thrush is one of the boldest defenders of its property, attacking the thieving Crow or Magpie, but the best security for all species is attained by the habit of the bird of close sitting. The females of Ring-Ousel and Blackbird are browner and less conspicuous than their glossy black mates, but this difference is not noticeable in the browner Thrushes, yet the bird crouching low behind the nest wall is not easy to see ; her eye is the brightest spot.

The Redstart has a very easily seen blue egg, but she nests in a hole ; the Nightingale has a deeply coloured olive-brown egg, and the situation of the nest in thick herbage aids invisibility. Stonechat and Whinchat bury their nests well in the herbage, and the blue egg of the Pied Flycatcher and the spotted red egg of the Spotted Flycatcher are seldom visible from the outside. A hole protects the very pale blue egg of the Wheatear, but the deeper blue of the Hedge-Sparrow requires the sober tints of the sitting parent to hide it.

In certain of the *Passeres*, the House- and Tree-Sparrows for instance, birds whose light eggs are hidden in covered nests, one of the clutch is almost invariably more lightly marked than the others. A similar variation is usual in the Sparrow-Hawk's eggs. Such variation, especially in the nests of Larks and Pipits, may lead to the idea that the nest contains the egg of a Cuckoo, but the expert eye, with the aid of a hand lens, can tell by the texture of the egg shell if this is the case.

The variously coloured eggs of the Cuckoo, approaching to certain types of fosterers, provide food for thought, and are responsible for many heated ornithological discussions. One thing is certain, that there are some female Cuckoos that invariably lay eggs that resemble in general colour the eggs of some particular species which is often victimised. Thus we have what Mr Chance calls Pipit-Cuckoos, Robin-Cuckoos, Hedge-Sparrow-Cuckoos, and others, and he believes, that when these specialised eggs, imitations of those of some other bird to put it baldly, are found in a nest of a species with which they do not agree, it is due to an accident that will be against the chances of survival. Though I certainly have not studied the matter in the systematic manner of Mr Chance, I have found or seen quite as many instances of what we may call false assimilation as of good matches.

My theory, and it can only be a theory, is that the parasitical habit is of comparatively recent origin, and that it was when it was in the making that natural forces, the weeding out of dissimilar eggs by the foster parents, moulded the colour to type. Each female retains the hereditary tendency to lay a certain type, resembling that of the foster parent in whose nest her ancestors invariably laid, but she will continue to lay in the nest of a species that brought her up. Where say a Robin type of Cuckoo's egg is found in a Hedge-Sparrow's nest (or any other dissimilar types) it may mean that at some period in that Cuckoo's ancestry a female Cuckoo failed to find an unoccupied Robin's nest when it was necessary for her to lay. She found a Hedge-Sparrow, and when the young Cuckoo matured she looked for the foster species that she knew, not the ones whose eggs would be like hers. This is not exactly inheritance of acquired characters but an accidental change of habit.

The two eggs of the Nightjar are placed upon the ground without any attempt at a nest. It is difficult to determine if they are protectively coloured or not, for the bird does not pay particular attention to the situation in which she dumps them, though she does like to stick, year after year, to the same locality, even the same spot. They are very beautifully marbled with unobtrusive colours, and if they are placed on bare ground where pebbles abound, or, as I have seen them, on a heap of stones, they are not easy to see; but on dead fern or bracken they are very conspicuous. But here the colouring of the parent comes in, for there is no better avian instance of protective colour than that of the Nightjar. Her delicate greys and browns melt into the surroundings; she is almost invisible, and remains so still when we are close to her that one can well imagine that she knows it. Even her bright eye is not wide open, but she watches us through a slit, as if half asleep.

In many of the Raptorial birds, the Merlin is a good example, the warm reddish colouring—blotches, smears, or eggs almost self-coloured with fine red specks—gives a suggestion of protection. The same applies to the ground-nesting Red and Black Grouse, especially to the former. It is interesting to note that in these two groups, in no ways related, the red colour is fugitive. Egg-collectors know that however dirty the eggs may be it is not safe to wash them when they are fresh, and risky later.

The eggs of most Wading Birds are distinctly protectively coloured, and they are laid in places where this is an advantage. Curlew, Dunlin, Snipe, Lapwing, Golden Plover have eggs of a darker style than some others; their marking has to assimilate with the surrounding vegetation. Those of Stone-Curlew, Ringed Plover, Oyster-catcher, and in another group, many of the Terns are, if we may so express it, designed for sandy surroundings; they are light coloured, and are exceedingly difficult to detect on sandy ground where there are pebbles, and practically invisible on a pebble bank.

The eggs of the Moorhen are not protective, but those of the Coot, its near relative, closely resemble the colouring of the blades that are used for nesting material; the fine speckles of rust or smut on the plants are represented by the black specks upon the grey-brown shell.

YOUNG REDSTARTS.

Colour has run riot in two species, the Guillemot and Razor-bill, especially in the former. No two eggs are exactly alike, and the grounds vary from bright green or blue, through browns and greys, to white; the markings may be blotches, spots, zones, patches or lines. It is by no means proved that any particular type of egg is hereditary, but the Yorkshire "climmers" know that the same bird will continue, year by year, to lay the same type, and usually on the same ledge. The explanation of this great variability is not certain, but it is argued that the Guillemot is very safe from foes on its precipitous cliffs, and that there is nothing to restrain the natural law of infinite variation. One thing supports this view, the fact that the bird lays only a single egg.

This brings us to another important oological problem. Why do the number of eggs laid by a bird vary in the different species? For answer we must look at the whole animal and vegetable kingdom—

> And finding that of fifty seeds
> She often brings but one to bear;

we are faced with one of the most appalling of all Nature's laws; to preserve the balance between species, it is necessary that on the average each pair of animals shall produce, in the whole of its life, but two offsprings that shall attain maturity. All the rest must perish, for if this average is exceeded for only a few generations, the population will outgrow the accommodation—the food supply—and many other interdependent species will suffer.

The number of young produced by each species must be just sufficient to allow these two (of course on an average) to survive, and the greater the dangers that face the young the larger the number of eggs or young required. The sporting

D

chances are against some, and in the favour of others, and as the Guillemot lays a single egg we can safely argue that it has a fairly safe youthful existence. Between this and the ten or a dozen of the Pheasant, the dozen and a half of the French Partridge, or the occasional two dozen of the Blue Tit, there is no end of variation; but we can be sure that the drain will regulate the family, or we shall see an increase. Rather more than the number that ought to survive are escaping infantile perils in some cases; this must be so with the increasing Starling, but we may feel sure that if left to itself Nature will put things right. We sorrow over the silly youngster which runs into danger and perishes; we should sorrow more if all survived, for we should have no food crop and we should go under.

DARTFORD WARBLER.

CHAPTER IV

The Nestling.   The Helpless Group

THE most specialised birds, those which are counted as ranking
high in the zoological scale, are, as we have seen, in a very helpless condition when they leave the egg shell.   When the open-
eyed, down-clad, precocious youngster saws its way through the
shell with its egg-tooth, and struggles out, sometimes with a
little cap of shell sitting on its fluffy back, there is so much
vigour and intention about its movements that an idea of dawn-
ing intelligence is suggested.   But when the blind, helpless " bald
pottling," as the boys call it, makes its debut, reflex action or
instinctive struggle is the only gift with which we can credit so
undeveloped an infant.

The appearance of the passerine bird that has just left the
egg is so unattractive, so ungainly, that it is not often figured;
whatever its parents may think, for ideas about new born babes
are vastly different from the standpoint of the parent and non-
parent, most observers will hardly dare to call this infant beautiful.   It is nearly naked and its bare skin is livid and unhealthy
in colour; its head is abnormally large, so are its feeble feet,
whilst its wings do not give any idea of organs of flight.   The
wing, at this stage, is a shapeless hand, without visible fingers
and with a mere apology for a thumb; it is attached to the
shoulders by a flap of skin which looks as if it was intended to
restrain rather than assist freedom of action.

The neck is scraggy, the body bloated and ends abruptly,

43

the graduation apparent when the tail is there is lost.   The beak looks blunter than it really is, for the cavernous mouth is fringed with skin folds, often brightly coloured, and very soon blue feather sheaths show on the edge of the hand-like wing-stump. The body, especially on the upper side, shows pitted tracts or areas, for these will give rise to the feather covering, so characteristic of the bird.   By the second or third day in the life of a quickly maturing bird of the helpless nestling group the flight feathers, still in bluish sheaths, lie in a row on the inner edge of the arm, and a few days later a tuft appears like a small stiff shaving brush at the bottom of the back.

The distribution of the down varies greatly, even in closely allied birds, and in quite a number—the Jay, Long-tailed Tit, and Dartford Warbler, and some of their near relatives for example—it is absent.   In most there is a little down round the closed eyes and some on the top of the head, where it is often long though scanty ; there is a strip down the middle of the back, and there may be some on the shoulders, wings and legs, sometimes forming a garter just above the tarsus.   Some shade of grey is most usual ; it varies from a pure grey in the Linnet or greyish white in the Willow-Wren to brownish in the Meadow-Pipit and black in the Creeper and Hedge-Sparrow.   The Grey Wagtail, amongst birds particularly studied in this book, has the most attractive down of golden buff.

The flanges or folds of skin on either side of the gape, beside being ample, are usually coloured.   It is true that in the Dartford Warbler, a downless youngster with very dark bare skin, the flanges are dull yellow, but in most birds they are brighter ; they are not, however, except in a few cases, so highly coloured as the skin of the inside of the mouth.   Thus the Yellow-hammer and Reed-Bunting have a pink mouth and yellow flanges, in the

Grey Wagtail the mouth is orange, and in the Meadow-Pipit carmine, but in both the outer fringe is pale yellow.

The object of a coloured mouth, yellow in most birds, is said to be a guide to the parent to make a good shot with the food it brings when the site of the nest is shaded or gloomy.   No doubt there is something in this, but it is also certain that some species that nest in dark surroundings have not the most illuminated mouths.   The Dartford Warbler nests in a very dense bush, but the inside of the mouths of the young are dull.   Those of the newly hatched Creepers are yellow, and not a very bright yellow, but the young Linnets in their well lighted nest have deep orange gapes.   Spots on the tongue and palate, found in a few species, are also claimed as guiding marks, but the birds that one would imagine would need them most have no such spots.   The Hedge-Sparrow, the Bearded Tit and some other birds have them, and the tongue of the Reed-Bunting is almost white at the end of the root-barbs and the tip ; their presence is too uncertain for any sound deductions.

Whatever guide the coloured gape may be to the attendant parents it is certain that the ample flanges must be useful, preventing spilling, serving in fact as infantile bibs.   When the mother bird appears with food she may utter a subdued announcement, or she may merely stir a twig by alighting upon it ; the effect is instantaneous.   Until her arrival the nest was at peace, every youngster snuggled inert in the cup ; they would lie there without stirring so long as she remained away.   But at the signal every skinny neck shoots up to its full extent, and every mouth is open wide in mute appeal.   The nest is filled with coloured tunnels, the big heads shaking tremulously like those of aged and infirm people.   The dole is presented and accepted, and the head collapses as the food passes with a gulping effort

down the narrow throat. This spasmodic response to a sound
can be produced by the feeblest imitation of a bird note or by
merely stirring a leaf with the finger, and if we do nothing head
after head sinks back into the shoulders or wearily droops, but if
a finger is thrust into a gaping throat it is gulped at with as
much enthusiasm as if it was a fat worm.

Now we understand the use of the flanges, for the mandibles
are as far apart as the flange will allow; it stretches from tip to
tip of the short bill, so that the mouth is the round end of an
open funnel.

As we shall see later, the precocious young bird looks for
food and learns by experiment what is good to eat and what
undesirable, but the helpless nestling is at the mercy of the food
provider; it accepts whatever is offered. Instinctive and purely
unconscious trust in parental wisdom does not lead to many
errors, but if we present some indigestible matter the infantile
stomach sees that it is speedily returned.

For some days, and indeed until the first contour feathers
are beginning to appear, the words of the great Dr Watts about
agreement in the nest are applicable; the youngsters are capable
only of the effort to lift their open mouths. The mother, and
more rarely the father, broods them from time to time, warming
them after their chilly wait when she was seeking food, but it is
only when they are beginning to feel the activities of young life
in the blood that they appear to be conscious of cold; then they
shrug and shift uneasily, always striving to snuggle down, however much the effort may incommode the others. As they grow
older and stronger the effort to obtain the first mouthful brought
by the parent causes constant nest disturbance, and it is by no
means unusual for one, stronger or more active than its bed-
fellows to raise itself and actually trample on the others. The

Young Birds (not drawn to scale).

1. Black Grouse.
2. Cuckoo.
3. Great Crested Grebe.
4. Coot.

5. Gadwell.
6. Puffin.
7. Common Tern.
8. Peregrine Falcon.

9. A typical Altricial, still blind.
10. Cormorant, first stages.
11. Golden Plover.
12. Bittern.

parent probably knows whose turn it is to be fed, and ignores the selfish grabber, for if this was not the case there would be far more instances of starvation of weaklings than there are. Young birds in their anxiety to be fed, or through the struggles of their companions, do fall out or get ejected from the nest, and it is remarkable how little this loss affects the parents.

The ability of birds to count has been discussed over and over again, and it cannot be proved one way or the other; the fact that a bird will go on laying, or that certain species will, if one egg at a time is taken out of a clutch, suggests that the bird does know the maximum that Nature thinks desirable to withstand the dangers of youth; but the fact that a mother bird will continue to feed the remnant of her brood when one or two lie slowly starving on the ground below, and that she makes neither effort to feed them nor to return them to the nest, proves that she is either incapable of realising the loss or is too philosophical to worry about it.

Entirely different is the parental behaviour when the young are older and have reached the age when they leave the nest. Her solicitude is then marked, for if one gets out before its due time it receives just as much attention and food as those still in the home. But by that time the young have learnt to express their feelings by other than the head method; in youthful bird language they tell her that they are hungry, and tell her persistently. Her maternal instincts respond to the calls; she cannot help herself, and must attempt to satisfy them. It is very easy to read into the ways of birds the various beautiful thoughts, actions and feelings associated with human maternal love, but we must remember that we know so little about bird psychology that it is dangerous to draw conclusions; the indifference of later life proves that whatever it is that stirs the affections during the infancy of the young, ceases to operate with a suddenness which is almost alarming. The bird is a perfect mother up to a point, and for a limited time. She sets a wonderful example of self-sacrifice, but she does not keep it up.

The altricial or helpless nestlings include many other than the passerine kinds, and it is hardly surprising to find that a bird that depends upon, and exploits, passerine species, should agree with them in its early youth. The Cuckoo as a nestling differs little from these fosterers; it is blind, helpless, entirely dependent upon parental care. And yet there is the one extraordinary difference, the existence in its purely instinctive soul of the desire and ability to get rid of its nest mates, and so gain in the struggle for existence.

What happens is now an old story, treated as the veriest myth when it was first described by Jenner, Montagu and Blackwall, even doubted when Mrs. Blackburn made her accurate sketches, and only really believed by the man in the street when photography, aided by the cinema, showed him pictures. It is a marvel, more wonderful than the method by which the parasitical adult deposits her egg or victimises only one species; more wonderful than the whole parasitical habit, strange though that is; for this blind, apparently helpless, and purely instinctive infant, when it is at its weakest, gets rid of its mates with devilish ingenuity.

Like the others in the nest all that it has at first either energy or initiative to perform is that same neck stretching, mouth opening, convulsive demand for food. But from the very first the infant is a fidget, and apparently its sensitive skin cannot stand the feel of either egg or young bird alongside; in the hollow of its back, a very distinct hollow, is one spot which if touched rouses a strange reflex response, and if in its uneasy shuffling in the nest either egg or nest-companion is lifted so as to lie on this spot the impulse to act is started. At once, with its thin neck and heavy head hanging, the little demon hunches up its shoulders, stiffening itself on its rather long legs ; longer now in proportion than they appear in after life. Slowly the infant Cuckoo backs up the slope of the nest cup, no longer striving to throw its victim off its back, and aiding itself with the hand-like wing-stumps, pawing at the nest material behind its back, climbs to the lip. Balancing itself for a moment as if to take breath it gives one special heave, and if, from the Cuckoo's point of view, it has luck, over goes its burden. Apparently exhausted, and well it may be, it sinks back to the bottom of the nest, and if there are others to be disposed of repeats the operation so soon as it has recovered from the first effort. It is a remarkable fact that if, in its early days, it fails to get rid of its nest companions, it will live at peace or comparative peace with the survivors. As a rule it thereafter reigns alone, demanding incessantly for more and more food, as it grows bigger and more ferocious in appearance, and usually much bigger than its fosterers.

When its first nest plumage is covering its naked body, for the Cuckoo has no down, it has a habit of puffing out its newly acquired plumage until it looks far too big for the small nest. If we approach it no longer throws up an open gape, but puffs and hisses as if to frighten an intruder away, and if it was not such an absurd little fraud we might imagine that its fierce peck could really do us injury.

The Swift, the Kingfisher, and the Woodpeckers, are like the Cuckoo, without down, and all are reared as helpless young under shelter or in holes. But the Nightjar, which belongs to this same group, is well covered with long down, reddish brown in colour.   There is no nest and the young when it has emerged finds itself on the bare ground; unlike its relatives it shares many characters of the precocious nestlings, and at a very early age will move about, creeping prone, using its wings as arms, like some small furry quadruped.   Nevertheless, this semi-precocious babe seems to have no ideas of feeding itself; it depends entirely upon the attentions of its parents.   The young Swift nests practically on the flat, and is active early, but it cannot walk, and its future hopes depend upon the rapid growth of the long flight feathers.   The Woodpeckers and Kingfisher are active enough when their plumage is growing, the former climbing the inside of the nesting hole and clinging to the lip of the entrance, looking out eagerly for the insect laden parent. The Kingfishers, too, will scramble down the dirty tunnel to the mouth, and there sit in a crowd, clad in prickly feather stumps like little porcupines, craving for fish.

In the Owls the first down plumage is white, and practically the whole body is covered; the facial disc, so strong a character of the mature bird, and which certainly adds to the bird's " wise " appearance, is only slightly indicated.   The true shape of the skull is noticeable in these very young birds, for the curious arrangement of the feathers in the old bird is as yet undeveloped. Thus a rather long and heavy hooked beak projects beyond the eyes, whereas in the mature Barn, Tawny or Long-eared Owl, this is hidden by the ridge of stiff feathers that divides the facial disc on either side of the beak.   In consequence the eyes look more lateral, more like those of other birds, than when they are set, both looking to the front, in the flattened face disc, with its diverging feathers.   In the Tawny and Long-eared Owls the white down is soon replaced by the first juvenile downy dress, darker and striped or barred.   The two birds are very much

YOUNG LONG-EARED OWLS.

alike in the nestling dress, but even from the first the face of the Long-eared Owl looks more oval, and consequently longer or narrower, than that of the Tawny.

The Merlin may be taken as an example of what happens in the nestling clothing of most of the falcons and hawks. The down is at first white, and as a matter of fact consists of two kinds of down, distinguishable both in form and origin, and some of this first down is replaced by the first feathers, and some, in about a fortnight's time, by a much greyer down. Tufts of the first nestling down stick to the tips of the growing feathers, and the young Merlin is a somewhat patchy and untidy little object. It is, of course, some time before these raptorial birds, which have to work hard to overtake and kill their prey, are able to do without parental help; they are certainly of the helpless class.

The infantile Heron and Bittern are the quaintest little objects, the former with an upstanding crest of stiffish feathers, brownish at the base, white towards the untidy tips. As in the raptorial birds the face is partly bare. This bare skin, not only on the face but on the neck, breast and underparts, of the young Bittern is a livid blue, and the down, long but nowhere thick, is a soft fawn, rising in a wind-stirred crest on the head, and long but sparse elsewhere on the body. When the youngsters sit upright with uplifted blue-green bills, looking at the observer with anything but angelic eyes, the effect is not only extraordinary but ludicrous; an accurately imitated juvenile Bittern would excel the most extravagantly manufactured gollywog in absurdity.

The little Cormorant begins life as a very naked infant, sooty brown in colour, but it quickly gets the necessary down covering, and a very thick brown covering it is. It is a woolly looking infant, but not nearly so woolly as its relative the Gannet, which also begins life with a black skin, but with a little whitish down to start with.   Its full white down looks all the whiter because the skin round the base of the bill, and eyes, and on the chin, remains bare.   Its subsequent changes are interesting and will be dealt with later.   The Petrels, born in holes, where they might be thought to be warm and sheltered, are clothed in thick down, and they have two successive coats.   The Petrels and the Manx Shearwater depend entirely upon the visits of the parents until they have grown feathers and are able to fly.   It seems that to a great extent the young are fed at night, and that they have to spend the day waiting for the return of the old birds, who have been seeking food, and storing it ready to disgorge as oil for the tender young digestions.   This may be so in many cases, but it is not the invariable habit, as I have taken both the sitting bird and the young from the same hole.

The Pigeons, with a hairy down, complete the list of the British Altrices or Nidicolae, as they have been called, or those birds that are helpless when young and are of necessity confined to the nest so long as they need parental attention to feed them or keep them warm.   Some ornithologists include certain birds that are born with open eyes, but it is evident that no real classification of helpless or precocious young can be made on the strength of any one single character.   Indeed, it is a very artificial division, as illustrated by the exceptional behaviour of the young Nightjar, but it has value in respect to the size of the egg and the independence of those that emerge from the larger egg.

CHAPTER V

The Nestling. The Precocious Group.

ALL the birds in the Nidifugae or precocious group come into the world with vision—their eyes are open when they leave the egg. All begin life with a downy dress, more or less of a complete covering, and within a very short time they feel their legs, to use a well known expression. But the great difference between members of this go-ahead group and the other is that they can, for some time, starve quite comfortably; they do not immediately require food from the parent, nor is it necessary for them to seek it for themselves. Stored within their bodies is a sufficient amount of yolk, the food within the egg, to nourish them without further aid. The families of British birds which, in the opinion of most who have worked out this somewhat artificial division, should be included, are the Geese and Ducks, the Grebes, Divers, Game Birds, Gulls, Bustards, Rails, and in particular the Waders.

When the little nidifugous bird leaves the egg it has several lessons that must be learnt quickly; it may have to fly (not literally) or escape from the place in which it first saw the light at a very early age; it must dry its damp down as quickly as it can, and get on its baby feet. The little Teal may have smashed its imprisoning envelope some yards from the water, but the water, without doubt, is its natural element, the place in which it will be safer than on weasel and rat-haunted land. Not that the Teal will find an aquatic life without dangers, by

any means ; the birds of prey are ready to pick it from the water ;
the pike, with rows of cruel teeth, lurk in the weeds ; even its
big and stately relation, the Swan, may worry its life out as a
terrier worries a rat.   Yet the mother Teal believes in the safety
of the water, for from the surface she has a better view of what
is around her than when, protected only by her own plumage,
she sat in the down-lined nest amongst the rough grasses.   Anything, unseen, might suddenly pounce upon her.   Therefore, as
soon as all the eggs which are going to hatch have emptied out
their living contents, she intimates in her own way that they
must be moving, and at once the ducklings stand on their untried
feet and stagger through the obstructing jungle to the water.
Their baby feet are webbed, but they need no swimming
instructor ; instinctively they take the water, instinctively they
paddle with alternate strokes.

We have taken as one example of the ducks that fine bird
of the shore and tidal estuary which systematists place between
the geese and ducks proper, the Sheld-duck, or as it is often
spelt, irrespective of sex, the Sheldrake.   Its nest, as we have
seen, is usually in a rabbit burrow or similar deep hole on sandy
dunes, in banks, or even high on the top of some small un-
frequented island.   The duckling leaves the shell in the dark ;
its eyes are open but surely it cannot pierce the gloom of the
deep burrow, six, ten or more feet from the open air.

The mother bird provides no food, but she must lead them
to the sea, where on sand or mud flat they will for themselves
find food.   She does not work alone, for though so many male
ducks refuse to take any share in domestic matters, the drake
of this species watches over the young, and certainly helps to
conduct them to the shore.   The journey is at times a long one ;
it is always attempted, and the youngster carries within it its

BITTERN AND YOUNG.

own rations, like the camel with its water supply. These infant Shield-ducks are unsophisticated ducklings when they begin their first long tramp; one brood that I encountered when they had just emerged from the burrow came trotting up, cheeping like farmyard ducklings coming to be fed; they allowed me to pick them up despite the frenzied performances of their alarmed guardians. Other matters relating to these very interesting ducks must be left for a later chapter.

The Golden Plover, as a representative of the moorland-haunting waders, has to learn very rapidly some method of avoiding danger, for the swift-winged Merlin beats the heathery tops, and the great Buzzard circles and soars on rounded wing high overhead, its long-sighted eyes on the look out for movement in the herbage far below. The down dress of the infant is its protection, for it is beautifully mottled with black on a golden-yellow ground, and white streaks break up the pattern. If danger threatens the bird responds to the warning note of the watchful parents and at once crouches and remains still; the moving juvenile might catch the eye, but the crouching youngster, as I can certify, is wonderfully hidden amongst the greens, yellows and browns of the upland vegetation. The little Red-shank, another wading bird of the Sandpiper, not the Plover group, has the same instinctive habit of "freezing" when in real or imagined danger; its down is buff and streaked longitudinally with brownish-black, and like the Golden Plover its underparts are white or slightly tinged with buff. Its haunts are meadow lands, often where the grass is long and withered by the sun, and the colours again harmonise with the surroundings.

The Common Snipe, when juvenile, has rich tawny, almost orange down, dusted at first with frosty white tips, and the young of the Woodcock, the bird selected as representing this group, is paler but has the same rufous tone. The longitudinal stripes and the darker patches that make up the pattern on the buff ground, are russet or almost chestnut. What are the surroundings in which this newly hatched babe must conceal itself? They are ruddy brown, for the bird is born as often as not in a thick bed of withered leaves.

The young Grebes come into the outer world in a complete suit of short, close down, well calculated to keep the small bird dry. In very many young birds in down the markings are arranged in more or less regular stripes, though in some of them the stripes are broken or extended so as to give a more mottled appearance; it may, however, be said that the longitudinal stripe is a character of the down plumage. In the ducks this pattern is not uncommon, but the long dorsal stripe has often cross streaks; there is great variation in this arrangement of markings, and the first dress of some young ducks is self-coloured. In the young Sheld-duck the dark stripes and cross bars on the light ground are very perfect, and the whole design is attractive. The chocolate marks spread over the crown, and a line follows the back of the neck to the shoulders, where there is a cross pattern to the wings; after that the line narrows again and runs to the tail. A second cross bar extends over the thighs, and in most young birds this is not quite connected with the dorsal streak. In many of the young waders the same streaky pattern with latitudinal bars or patches prevails, but the proportion of light and dark down varies considerably.

In the nestling dress of the Great Crested Grebe the stripes reach their greatest perfection, the dark colour being black or very dark brown, and the lighter grounds white to buff. The series of stripes running down the back is very regular, but those on the neck are the more noticeable because the ground is paler,

SAND MARTIN.

and they also persist long after the other markings have been obliterated by the growth of the juvenile plumage. Framed by a neat pattern of glossy black is, on the front of the crown, though not actually on the forehead, a small triangle of bare vermilion skin. The use and origin of this patch, which vanishes as the small bird grows, has not so far been discovered; there is nothing to correspond with it in the mature bird.

The small Teal is hatched in a warm, down-encircled, dry nest; the young Sheld-duck in the cosy seclusion of the burrow; both are ready to enter chilly water without parental education or compulsion. The tiny Grebe struggles from the egg to find itself on a soaking raft of water-logged, rotting vegetation, and surely it might be expected that so moist a nursery would teach an exceedingly aquatic species that the water, on or in, was its future and natural home. Not at all; the first effort of the nestling is to get away from such uncomfortable surroundings, and it makes use of its newly discovered activity in an attempt to scramble to the back of the parent which happens to be on the nest when it emerges, for unlike ducks, both male and female take their turn in brooding. The lobed feet do not look suitable climbing organs, but aided by bill and arms it scrambles over the parental apology for a tail, and gains the cradle prepared for it by the old bird. The little one snuggles between the slightly raised wings of the adult bird, and much of its early life is spent upon the back of the parental steed. Cygnets share this habit, and the upraised wings of the old Swans give them a tent as shelter.

Whatever the plumage of the adult Rails, the young in their down dress are self-coloured, blackish grey or sooty; even the Spotted Crake and the Water-rail, birds with elaborate plumage, have these self-coloured infants. The mature Moorhen is brown,

E

the old Coot greyish black, but in these two the heads of the
downy young are coloured when they are very juvenile. The
frontal plate of the Moorhen is sealing-wax red, that of the Coot
a dead white, and the tiny plate on the foreheads of both
juveniles is red, but in the Moorhen the little beak is orange
with a yellow tip, in the Coot it is white with a black tip. On
the face of the first nestling is a little naked skin with sparse
hoary down, but the crown is livid blue, and the nape orange.
Round the bill of the little Coot are orange warts or papillae,
with orange down, and the head is blue, passing to orange or
vermilion, though the colours vary.

The small Moorhen is very active when first hatched, and
when only just free of the shell will scramble about in the nest,
climbing over the rim and diving instinctively if warned by the
parent. Climbing comes naturally to it, for there is in its early
days a very distinct claw on the thumb; it uses its hands, and
will clamber up even a steep bank, making full use of its claw.
Claws or nails persist in many young birds; they are certainly
a survival from reptilian ancestors.

Young Gulls remain longer in the nest than many of their
relatives; indeed it would be hard for the juvenile Kittiwake to
do anything else, for its playground is restricted. Where other
cliff-nesting gulls, as the Herring gull or Lesser Blackback,
nest on the flat or on broad grassy ledges, the young will leave
the nest at an earlier age, and if in danger crouch like a little
wader amongst the herbage. The down patterns of gulls are
more broken into mottles than those of waders, and it is remarkable that the browns and blacks, with buff or grey grounds, are
much paler and less emphatic in the Kittiwake than in those
birds whose existence depends more upon their habit of seeking
concealment. Exactly the same thing happens with the Terns,

CUCKOO IN NEST OF REED-WARBLER.

some of which are dark, some light when in down. Indeed the young Arctic, Common and Sandwich Terns vary greatly, but follow two marked types, so that they have been described as dimorphic.

Now the origin of dark or light colours is almost certainly the need for concealment, and as some of these birds nest on dark rocks or amongst herbage, and others on sandy ground, it is easy to see that a young one with a dark buff ground, mottled with still darker shades, will be hidden in one situation, and a lighter bird be protected on sandy surroundings. On the whole the young of the Sandwich Tern, which prefers the dunes, is lighter than that of either of the other two. But what do we find? An adult bird, aware that her eggs will be dark or light, or that certain surroundings will suit the nestling? If this is so the birds are exceedingly stupid, for the dark form on the light ground, and the light on rock or in herbage, is as common as the perfect match. The birds know nothing about it and care less.

These apparent failures of Nature to complete the work she has begun, or to carry out a rule which has been evolved during many strenuous generations and at great loss to the species are very puzzling. Dr Chalmers Mitchell has given us an enlightening sentence: "Existing colours and patterns of eggs and of animals may be survivals from circumstances in which they were useful." Changed conditions and a less strenuous early life may have rendered the special protection unnecessary, but the dimorphic forms are retained by heredity. Very likely the perfection of the colonial habit is responsible, for the Terns are plucky birds, and an enemy that would not be driven away by a single Tern may refuse to face a colony. Irate adult Terns will kill the foolish young Blackheaded Gulls which ramble across the sacred ground; they will even kill a rabbit, they will threaten a man, and I have seen them defeat a cow which unwittingly might have trampled on eggs and young.

In most birds, and especially in the Gulls and Terns, the protective markings and colour of the young are lost when the first plumage is attained. Gulls take longer to reach maturity than Terns, but in the first dress they are still mottled, for dangers are not over until the birds can fly; even when the power of flight enables them to ramble over sea and shore, these big dark birds may be seen, and it is a curious fact that when in this mottled dress of immaturity they actually look bigger than their parents.

One of the characters of the precocious birds is that they are, at an early age, independent of parental care, but this does not mean that the parents believe this and cease to feed them; nor do the young appear to wish to believe it, for they continue to be dependent as long as they can. The young Kittiwake on its tiny ledge, or in a nest that seems without visible support, cannot obtain food for itself; there is some excuse for it. But the staggering young Herring-Gull could find something to interest it even if not to fully nourish it; yet the calls of these big babies in the colony are clamorous, and the Herring-Gull which has full powers of flight or swimming, will continue to whistle plaintively after its apparently indifferent mother, who for the sake of peace will occasionally give it supplies. It is true that when the young Gulls leave the nest they will sample all kinds of objects, pecking at pebbles, or pulling bits off the low-growing herbage; they are teaching themselves by experiment, and perhaps it is well for the young experimenters that the species is practically omnivorous.

Whether the very young Grebe could if it would find and over-

French or Red-legged Partridge.

take its finny prey is doubtful, but it is certain that it is reluctant
to make the attempt.   As we shall see later the diving habit is not
easily acquired, and the bird is fed by the parents, often, as shown
in the illustration, when on the back of the other member of the
pair.   Long after it has learnt to dive it will swim, with constant
insistent whistles, after the old bird, who escapes from this
persecution by taking lengthy dives, leaving the striped-necked
young one peering over the water to see where its elusive parent
will reappear.

The longitudinal stripe pattern is shown in the Game Birds,
and the colours and markings are more pronounced in the Grouse
than in the Partridge.   In the Red-legged or French Partridge
the pale heads are without spots, but black-brown and yellow
are arranged in streaks on the back.   One of the most remarkable
points in the life history of both Common and Red-legged
Partridge is the early age at which the young get serviceable
wings ; the flight feathers come rapidly, and when the " cheepers "
are about half the size of the old birds they can rise and whirr
off into the long grass for safety, even though their efforts may
only carry them a few yards.   The diminutive tail is spread in
these youngsters in exactly the way that it is when mature birds
are flushed.

The Red-legged Partridge is well-known as a runner, and the
infants share this habit, and if they can find sufficient cover by
running will do this rather than trust to their short rounded
wings.   All very young Game Birds are active when hatched,
and though they are ready to try the crouching, motionless habit
of attempting to escape notice, they are gifted with enough
instinctive knowledge, or undeveloped reasoning power, to take
advantage of any long herbage or other handy shelter, for the
crouching attitude is more likely to save them when they are

surrounded by grass or other screening vegetation than when they squat in the open.   Indeed, in many open places the colour and markings of their down plumage would be fatally distinct. Some of the young Waders, Sandpipers and others, will however crouch immediately they have suspicion of danger, and they certainly pay no attention to the fact that they may be in full view or in the direct line of the approaching peril.   But of this more in the next chapter.

CHAPTER VI

Behaviour of the Young

In the previous chapter I referred to the habit of crouching for protective purposes as one of the instinctive habits of the precocious nestling. In a measure it is shared by the helpless group, for though they will at once respond to any sound, and put up their heads for food, so long as they are blind, they very soon learn that there is danger in any disturbance other than that caused by the approach of the parent. Probably most people would say that young birds in the nest are usually silent, but this is only true so long as they are little more than automata. So soon as their first juvenile plumage is attained, in which the body is clothed with what are termed contour feathers in addition to the growing quills of wings and tail, the little birds become in a measure intelligent, and call for food in weak but gradually strengthening voices whenever the pangs of hunger give occasion. It is true that these infantile voices are not often heard, but the explanation is that the parent on guard sees us before we see it in most instances, and at once gives a warning note, the meaning of which is understood by the young.

It is then that the nestlings "crouch" or "freeze" in the nest, keeping still and quiet until such time as the parent announces "all clear," which is the signal that conversation may begin once more. On the whole, however, the opportunity for interesting activity of the nestlings is not great in species which

63

have to remain within the restraining walls; it is not until they leave the nest that they have much to show us.

Crouching then is instinctive, practically reflex; it is the automatic response to the stimulus of the warning note, the parental intimation of danger. As the bird grows, undoubtedly, instinct becomes intelligence. The very young precocious bird, say the Golden Plover, as that is one we have taken as representing a group, will crouch at the first suggestion of need without any knowledge of where it is going to crouch, but as it grows it uses its eyes, and though it does not select a spot where its colours will match surroundings, it takes advantage of any clump of long grass or ling that will afford shelter. I have had a good deal of experience of the young of its relative the Lapwing, and when I was attempting to discover the young in order to "ring" them—that is to mark them with a numbered aluminium ring so as to trace their migration pathways—I found that a simple ruse was usually successful. Knowing where the young were in the habit of feeding with their parents, I crawled to a place where I could with the glass watch the youngsters; then, suddenly standing up, I startled both old and young; the former rose with pitiful cries of alarm, the latter vanished.

It is possible to mark down the exact spot where one young bird was last seen, and keeping one's eyes fixed on this spot to walk straight to it, but when you want to find four this means at least four separate journeys and a long wait between each disturbance. Also, it is very easy to fix an eye on a bird and find that it is one that is already ringed. After a while I saw that all that was necessary was to get the area in which the little birds were feeding, and then examine the roots of every thistle clump, the underlip of the ditches, and best of all the foot of a tall stone wall. How they managed to reach these

GOLDEN PLOVER.

shelters with such speed I never found out, but it was here that the little birds were crouching, and not one was in the open. The birds at the foot of the wall had a wonderful knack of ramming their fluffy bodies into the spaces between the stones, and there they remained still, head inwards, tail out.

The quickness with which young Ringed Plovers on a beach will learn the value of shelter is most interesting. On one beach the eggs were laid and hatched on the shingle ridge just above high-water mark, and at full tide the young birds were on the ridge. There, when the old bird gave the signal, the little ones sank down at once, for their greyish down closely assimilated with the many coloured pebbles; they would remain perfectly still, even when I lightly placed a foot above them. It would be too easy to crush these motionless youngsters underfoot did we not expect their presence. When the tide was out the birds followed their parents to the wet sand to seek for food, and there when the note of warning was uttered the young raced for shelter. Large stones or seaweed-covered rocks were what they made for, and they showed a very accurate knowledge of the geographical possibilities of the beach; they would dive under the overhanging tangle, even if it meant crouching up to their necks in a rock pool.

In the Ringed Plover and the Lapwing, but not in the Golden Plover, there is a white collar on the nape and neck, immediately behind a black band. There are two methods of crouching; in the one the little bird flattens itself down with the neck outstretched, in the other it squats, and the head is drawn back. The first position is always adopted by the Stone-Curlew, a bird that lives on chalk downs and open stony wastes; its parents also hide themselves in the same way, lying with neck extended when their isabelline shades render them most inconspicuous. The Ringed Plover usually crouches with the head drawn back so that the black line on the nape meets the grey down of the shoulders and the white collar is hidden, but I have found it in the other position, when the collar was decidedly conspicuous. The young Lapwing almost always hides its collar.

When the young Lapwing, Golden Plover or Ringed Plover has been discovered it may be picked up without showing any immediate sign of alarm, and some of these young birds will crouch if again placed on the ground, but as a rule the handling scares them and they begin to struggle and cheep. When released they usually run, and run very fast, often falling over in their hurry, for their little legs are not yet used to high speeds. The bird may crouch as soon as it imagines that it is safe, but it may continue to run to a great distance; if the species is a maritime one, it as a rule makes for the shore, where shelter is to be found, rather than towards the tide line. At Highcliffe, where there are low mud cliffs behind the somewhat shallow beach, I found that the young Ringed Plovers did not crouch on the shore, but ran at once towards the sloping clays at the foot of the cliffs, where they raced uphill with great speed and apparent intelligence, for in the numerous cracks, filled with tidal litter they easily found secure hiding-places. As the beach at the season when the young are able to run is much frequented, it is probable that the local race had found that safety was more sure if they ran before crouching than if they dropped into the prone position where they might be trodden on.

When the young of any wading-bird are running away, either before or after crouching, they have a curious habit which is not easy to explain. They make frequent dips towards the earth as if picking up food; in some cases the bill does actually touch the earth, in others it certainly does not, and the pro-

CORMORANT. Feeding young.

bability is that when the bird is really excited by the desire to escape it does not pick up food, even if it sees it. It is, however, possible that the act of picking up food is reflex, and that the bird, when young, however scared it may be, cannot refrain from pecking at anything that its eyes inform it is edible. When the old Lapwing is running from the neighbourhood of the crouching chicks, intending to lead the intruder from the danger zone, it will pretend to feed in exactly the same way, but in this case there is the distinct advantage to the bird that it may mislead its pursuer by the suggestion that it has not observed him. The young may have inherited an instinct which is of no value to them.

A very useful instinctive activity of young birds is that adopted by Ducks, some of the Rails, Auks, and a few other birds with aquatic habits. The young seek safety when threatened by diving, and will either come up after a swim under water, or if possible in the shelter of the waterside vegetation, or even beneath the banks. Ducks are divided into two big groups, those which seek food under water—the Diving Ducks, and those which feed by sifting mud through the plates on their bills, and are known, somewhat erroneously, as the Surface-Feeders. Now, we should imagine that young diving ducks would early learn to dive, but the immature surface-feeder shares the habit, and at the threat of danger goes under. It is worth noting that the mature Mallard or Teal, both surface-feeders, will dive for sport and for safety if wounded, and in both species the very young birds dive if in danger. Young Teal, however, when alarmed, and warned by the curious croaking quack of the mother, will race for the banks, actually running on the surface without their light bodies sinking; it sounds incredible, but we know that insects can travel on the surface film, and apparently ducklings, if they move swiftly enough, can run upon it without more than occasional splashing with their tiny feet.

Moorhens, Coots, Water-rails, and the smaller Crakes dive for safety if alarmed when only a few hours old; I cannot say if they share the remarkable habit of the old birds of submerging their bodies and keeping the head alone above water, remaining there hidden by the surrounding stems; they are, however, most difficult to discover when they have found shelter amongst the reed stems or in rushes.

Grebes, as we have shown, are in no hurry to take to the diving habit, and when they leave the nest do not attempt to escape in this way. It is, however, difficult to surprise these birds, for if danger threatens the old birds will lead them into the densest bed of rushes, sedges or reeds, where it is like looking for a needle in a haystack to search for so small and neatly striped a youngster.

Guillemot, Razorbill and Puffin are birds which do not take to the water very early, though the young of the first two are dropped into the sea by their parents before they can really fly. Once there, after the first alarming plunge, they take to diving as their life work.

Diving is not a common habit amongst Passerine birds, but one, the Dipper, finds much of its food under water. It will swim under water, or walk at the bottom, clinging to the stones. At what stage the habit is learnt I am not sure, but as certain instruction is given by parents in other matters, it is likely that by imitation the young Dipper learns how to find the aquatic insects, crustaceans and molluscs on which it has to subsist. One experience, however, is worth recording. I had scrambled up a steep bank to a Dipper's nest, which was situated under the grassy top, immediately above a deep pool.

COCK STONECHAT AND YOUNG.

When I put in my hand I found that the little birds were nearly fledged, though still unable to fly; they had not yet left the nest. I took out one for examination and two or three others of the brood came tumbling out, and dropped right into the water. They certainly had never been there before, but they dived at once, and one bird swam under water, and rising to the surface, made for the bank, where it crouched amongst the stones. Doubtless, the first plunge was involuntary and alarming, but the action of at once responding by swimming under water was very interesting, for when the young Dipper normally leaves the nest it can fly, and its wings are the organs it uses when it desires to escape from danger. It will, however, plunge into the water if threatened by a Merlin or other hawk.

Although the young precocious bird has, thanks to its internal store of yolk, something to go on with, it must very soon learn the art of finding food, and this is just as necessary a lesson for the birds of the other group when they leave the nest.

In the matter of feeding, instinct and experience influence the young bird's future. Instinct teaches the beginner that it must find and assimilate food, just as instinct impels the young of all mammals, including the human babe, to suck to obtain the mother's milk, and the blind, helpless bird to swallow what it has stretched up its head to receive. But when it is more or less left to its own resources, it is impelled by instinct to peck at anything that appears to be edible, but it has to learn to use discrimination; it will peck at stones and grit, and these if swallowed help in digestion, but they do not supply nourishment. It must find out, and find out soon, what objects are food, and food that suits it, and what must be left alone or need not be sampled; and this it does by experiment.

Whatever may be our views on the vexed question of Instinct

versus Reason, we cannot deny that all young animals have good memories; results of experiments, whether good or bad, leave a lasting impression, and remembered impressions are the bird's education. These impressions are by no means confined to matters that relate to food; they are recollections of all kinds of incidents in the brain storehouse which regulate the whole of its after life. The bird that is trying its wings for the first time attempts to alight on a too slender twig, and falls, fluttering through the branches; it may do this two or three times, but it soon learns to aim for one that will support its weight, and a full grown bird seldom makes the same error. The curious behaviour of the Sheld-ducks that had just emerged from the burrow for the first time has been mentioned; they had no fear of being handled, and were not alarmed until they found that their actions were restrained, but they scuttled off when released; I cannot say what those particular birds did in after life, but the behaviour of adult birds, and of young birds on the shore, proves that the instinct for self-preservation is very strong, and is soon learnt.

This brings me back to the diving habit amongst other recollections of young Sheld-ducks. A brood of young birds had been led from the burrow and were swimming with their parents on a lagoon, cut off by a seawall from the shore. Two men came along with a retriever, and the dog swam out to chase the apparently helpless birds; the old ones at once cleared off in alarm. The dog swam towards one of the ducklings and prepared to snap at it, but without any hesitation the bird dived and came to the surface behind the dog. The hunter then turned its attention to the nearest one that was still on the surface, and again was disappointed, and so the competition went on, dog swimming, ducks diving, and every time rising behind the dog's back. The ducklings showed very little sign of alarm,

WREN AND YOUNG.

and did not attempt to swim away, but only to escape by short dives, and finally a very weary dog was called from the water by its master, and the ducklings were left at peace. Ducklings on the sands, when they have learnt that a human being is to be avoided, will race on their short legs, holding their wing stumps out like running ostriches, and if pressed will show wonderful smartness in dodging; they will double and twist like hares.

Instinctive use of the normal method of progression is illustrated by young nestlings that have never been on the wing. I showed how the young Dipper will dive, but there are many species that if disturbed in the nest at once attempt escape by flight. It is affirmed by many bird students that all birds have to be taught to fly, and in a measure this is true, though the teaching is rather tempting them to an effort than showing them how to perform. But the lesson may be learnt in another way, by experience when alarmed. I climbed to a nest of a Raven in which was a full fledged brood, and I have had a similar experience with the Carrion-Crow. When approached the young birds instinctively crouched, flattening themselves down so as to be inconspicuous, but when my hand was close to the nest, they rose and without hesitation went over the edge. I do not know what happened to some of the young, for they went over a steep cliff towards the sea, but the air no doubt held them up, their wings acting as parachutes, and probably they drifted to some ledge without accident. One bird, however, fluttered along the cliff face, dropping slightly, and finally alighted, very scared, on a broad ledge above a bay, where, as it was afraid of again taking wing, I captured it.

Another case refers to a very different bird, the Willow-Wren. I had found a nest crowded with fledged young which had not so far ventured abroad, and I had waited until I judged that the moment was ripe to ring them, just before they left the nest. I took them out and put them in my pocket, ringed them in turn, and when all were marked, replaced them in the domed nest, holding my hand over the opening until they had once more settled down. I did not hold it long enough, for immediately I withdrew it the nest exploded like a bomb, and infantile Willow-Wrens fluttered off, flying a few feet or even inches before they floundered into the bracken and bushes. They strove to fly before they were ready. I left them, hoping that the anxious parents, who were calling pathetically from the branches, could collect the fugitives, but I fear that some of them would fall victims to the first weasel that came that way.

The time when the young Passerine bird leaves the nest is the most dangerous period of its life. It can just manage to fly, but it wearies quickly, and it has not yet learnt what object means danger. Also it believes that the old birds must be summoned to attend to its wants, and continues to utter its insistent calls for food, oblivious of the fact that it is advertising its presence to ears that are attentive, the ears of rapacious foes. The young Thrush or Robin flutters to a perch, and there sits with breast puffed out, looking more like a frog than a bird, and repeats again and again its demands for attention; with indecision in its expression it eyes our approach, and seldom makes up its mind to fly until a hand is within a few inches; then it will flutter off with a startled scream, and generally fails to find a perch, for its feeble wings do not lift it well, and will drop towards the ground rather than rise to the branches where it would be safe. It soon learns, however, that the elevated position means fewer excursions for safety, and in short flights aims for the higher branches.

Young Passerine birds are in no hurry to leave their parents,

Long-tailed or Bottle Tit.

nor do the mature birds at once get over the family attachments; the brood is conducted through the wood, over the fields, or along the hedgerows, and the frequent plaintive calls of the anxious parents prove the continuance of the parental instincts. There are few more attractive sights than a pair of mature Long-tailed Titmice or Wrens leading the family that has for good and all deserted the nest. The music of the pack consists of contented twitters mingled with short calls that undoubtedly imply requests for attention. The little birds whirr their tiny wings with quite unnecessary speed, and shoot at perches which they do not always reach, but they take great care not to lose sight of and touch with the conductors. The little " Bottle-tits " have absurdly short tails, which must have been an advantage when they were packed so tightly in the feather-full nest, but now are a disadvantage, for the long tail acts as a balancing pole, and materially assists in maintaining the centre of gravity when the short wings are in action. Hereditary rather than instinctive action is shown by the stumpy tails of the Wrens; as the little Wren hops from twig to twig after one of the old birds it constantly cocks the short feathers which will never grow very long. The young Grey Wagtail, which in after life makes such constant and characteristic play with its graceful tail, has a stumpy little fan of infantile feathers. In courtship the tail of the Grey Wagtail is elevated and spread so as to exhibit the white outer feathers to advantage, and when the birds are feeding before nesting has begun the tail is carried high, and is not so constantly sawed up and down, as is the habit of the Pied Wagtail. The infant raises its short tail, and fans it out, in exactly the same way.

Characteristic pose is of course hereditary, but it requires

F

practice to become perfect.   Birds that live amongst perpendicular stems, such as the Sedge-Warbler and the Reed-Bunting, have a noticeable method of perching.   One leg is held straight, gripping the stem directly beneath the bird, and the other is flexed, the foot grasping opposite the bird's body; the pose of the bird is upright, but slightly leaning to one side.   The young Reed-Bunting, when it first attempts to settle on the reeds, is apt to grip with both legs flexed, with the result that the body is not well supported and sags, or the infant swings round in the wind and as a rule lets go and tries again.   The best way to preserve a balance has to be learnt by the bird itself, though the instinctive knowledge must be there since the birds all attain it in time.

The instinct to protect itself by retaliation does not exist in all young birds, but it is very marked in some.   It is almost absent in the *Passeres*, and even the young Carrion-Crow or Jay will not attempt to peck if handled until well grown. A trapped Jay will scream and peck, but a young Jay, even when caught after it has learnt to fly, will do nothing more than utter doleful calls of alarm.   In birds of other orders there is great variation.   The young Cuckoo, for instance, an evil-tempered little beast that will peck at the foster parent that has just given it food, will strike at the hand with its bill, as it puffs out its feathers and hisses with anger.   Proverbially peaceful Doves, though they cannot do a man injury, will strike with bill and wing, and unfledged Turtle-doves in the nest are just as emphatic in their threats; it has often amused me to be buffeted by the weak wings of Turtles and Ring-doves.

The young Bittern, when it is getting its feathers, cannot be handled too carefully, for it has learnt by heredity that its spear-shaped bill is a useful weapon; the old bird can strike upwards with lightning speed and deadly aim, as the old falconers knew well, and when the enemy is human the bird aims for the eyes. The juvenile Bittern holds its bill ready and its neck slightly flexed, and will follow the custom of its ancestors, striking at the face. The beaks of Raptorial birds, though hooked for purposes of food rending, are not the weapons upon which they rely for defence; it is the sharp claws on the powerful legs that are their safeguards. Young Tawny or Long-eared Owls, Kestrels and Merlins, when in the nest or when disturbed in the open before they can escape, throw themselves on their backs and hold the legs flexed like boxers. I have seen a whole nest full of white young Merlins with each youngster on its back, its feet ready to strike, its hooked bill chattering defiance. I have known a captive young Tawny Owl, when in its juvenile plumage, to fly at and fix its claws in the hair of a girl who went into its cage, though I could handle it with impunity. It is true that the girl had a very fine crop of auburn hair, which perhaps annoyed it, but it is the method of attack in a young bird that is here specially interesting.

Play is characteristic of all young animals, and play, as in human beings at an early age, consists in imitation of the activities of after life. The young animal usually pretends to fight or to make love, but the sham fight or amorous passage are more characteristic, or more easily observed in mammals than in birds. When, however, the frequent desire for food is not the ruling passion, play does show itself. A brood of young Teal or other ducks will sport with one another in the water, diving and splashing in exactly the same way that their elders will indulge their overflowing spirits in the spring. Passerine birds when nearly ready to leave the nest will peck one another, and young Starlings when feeding together in flocks will engage in short fights, jumping at one another, pecking, and striking with the wings; but it is always difficult to distinguish between the mock fight and the natural peevishness and jealousies of birds. Young Pheasants and Partridges will fight like game-cocks, striking with the spurs, and this, almost certainly, is play. Courtship pretence is rarer, but I have seen Great Crested Grebes with their necks still decorated with the stripes of immaturity, rearing up in front of one another to fence or toy with their bills, in exactly the manner adopted by the adult birds when courting.

MALE CROSSBILL AND YOUNG.

CHAPTER VII

Behaviour of the Parents

THE behaviour of young birds depends largely upon the behaviour of the parents; they act in response to certain admonitions, call and warning notes, and also undoubtedly imitate the actions of the adult birds. The parental actions rather than those of other birds of the same species are what they copy; their attention is focused on the two that wait upon them and take care of them. It is this parental care that now interests us.

In care of the young the most important efforts of the old are those that have as their object protection from external dangers. These operations begin with the choice of the nesting site, and that aspect has been dealt with in a previous chapter. Next comes the care of the eggs, apart from the unconscious and hereditary concealment provided by colour or situation. In most cases the major share of this period of nursing falls upon the female bird, but in a very large number of instances the male takes his turn on the nest. The ducks as a group leave the brooding to the female, and her plumage being less conspicuous than that of the drake, makes this necessary. It is true that the male acquires what is termed an "eclipse" dress in summer, a much less showy garment than he wore in winter and early spring, but this is to give him personal security during the moult, for as his flight feathers are shed rather too quickly, he is often practically unable to fly, and lurks in the herbage, or well out in open water, screened by his temporary "undress."

77

The Great Crested Grebe, however, a bird frequently found on the same waters as Mallard and Teal, is very gallant in his domestic duties, relieving the female with great regularity. Many of the Passerine birds take a spell on the nest to give the hen a chance of obtaining food, but others mount guard as their chief duty. Very many cock birds—the Robin and Yellowhammer are good examples—bring food to the sitting hen, who may take it without leaving the eggs, or may come off the nest for a few moments and pose before her mate with open bill and quivering wings in the attitude of a young bird asking for food. For mated birds to feed one another during courtship is not uncommon, but this will be referred to later.

The old birds are, as a rule, less careful of eggs than of young, and this is well, for the disappointments of the too anxious mother of eggs must be many. The birds grow more and more assiduous to the care of their property as time passes. Nevertheless, from the time when the nest is built, or even before, the male mounts guard on his observation post. Amongst the *Passeres* no bird is more faithful to his look-out than the cock Stonechat; he selects some tall weed, or upstanding branch of a withy or other plant, and there, all day long, he spends a few seconds or even minutes between his sallies for food or excursions to help his mate. When she is sitting he is constantly on the watch, and if danger threatens, his quiet word of warning will give her the chance of slipping off, slinking through the herbage, and appearing at a distance from the nest to share the anxious observation of the intruder. The anxiety evinced by the male and female varies according to the state of incubation of the eggs, but even when these are fresh the birds fidget about from perch to perch, constantly uttering a sharp " tic."

The Sedge-Warbler and the Reed-Bunting, living in similar

and often the same territory, have several look-out posts, and during the nesting season these are occupied in turns, so that the bird gets varied views of the surroundings. In many species, the Redstart, Robin, Sedge-Warbler, Nightingale, and Wren, for example, the male sings from these perches when the hen is sitting, an expression of his feelings which may be less chivalrous than appears at first sight. Yet the male in song, and not giving warning cries, must create confidence; all is well so long as he sounds happy.

The moorland birds have their look-outs on mounds that rise above general level, and their distance from the nest depends upon circumstances. Thus the Merlin perches on some little hillock within sight of the nest, and never very far away; there he sits, his head sunk in his shoulders, occasionally turning his gaze on some passing Pipit, but always ready to lower his head as if to concentrate the powerful eyes on any distant figure that may spell intrusion. The Curlew rarely shows itself when it is on the watch, for it is a cautious fowl, but the Golden Plover stands, very upright, in some commanding position, as a rule a mound on the skyline. He remains there, calling a mellow and rather plaintive note, and unless we are uncommonly quick sighted we shall not see the female slip off the nest and run through the heather, but her answering note is the first intimation of her presence, and we discover her standing on another knob, much nearer to us, and in quite another part of the moor from her mate. The nest is probably between the two birds, but we can be quite certain that it is not very near either of them. If, however, we get "warm," as children say, both birds will approach, and calling more emphatically strive to draw our attention, as they deliberately lead us away from the danger zone.

Many birds sit until we are close to the nest, trusting that they will escape observation. Their behaviour if detected, or when their nerves can no longer stand the strain, is more frenzied when there are young than when eggs have to be guarded. The Ring-Ousel and Blackbird fly off with a startled rattling scream, thus giving away the locality of the nest, but other species, for example the Willow-Wren and Dartford Warbler, are very careful not to let themselves be seen until they are well away from the spot. Many birds adopt a most interesting method of luring the intruder away; it is technically known as "squattering," and was originally applied to the ducks.

"Awa ye squattered like a duck," says Burns, and in no bird is the habit more marked than in the Teal. Squattering is the simulation of disablement, and its object is, undoubtedly, to mislead the enemy into the idea that it has an easy, half-lame victim. The Teal quacks loudly and with an unusual intonation, and striking the water with its wings, flies low just above the surface, its lowered tail often helping to create water disturbance; the bird flops in with an intentionally heavy splash, rises again, still beating with its wings, and as long as we remain near the nest continues the performance.

Ground nesters use the trick more than those that nest in elevated positions; the Reed-Bunting is a constant squatterer when it has young in the nest. It will tumble about with whirring and seemingly dislocated wings, struggling through the undergrowth, and piping as if in pain. The Nightjar will also squatter, but if there is a branch at hand it will rise to that and perching along it give some extraordinary wing performances for our benefit, thus drawing our eyes from the ground where eggs or young lie.

The disability feigning performance reaches its perfection in

TEAL.

1, 2. Courtship Attitudes.
3. Duck squattering.
4. Drakes fighting during display.

some of the wading birds. The Common Sandpiper will slip quietly away if the nest contains eggs, but will tumble about as if in great distress if we suddenly come upon the young, but the Ringed Plover is a master, whirring about, a maze of feathers, like some unfortunate game-bird that has received a pellet in the motor portion of the brain. If we follow the struggling bird it will just manage to keep out of reach, and when we are far enough away from the young, will take wing with a call which is almost derisive. I have only seen the Golden Plover squatter once, and then I nearly put my foot on the nest; as a rule the sitting bird has left when the one on watch gave the alarm.

The Plovers as a rule try to lure one from the nest by quieter methods, showing themselves plainly and announcing their presence by plaintive calls; this is the usual course pursued by both Golden Plover and Lapwing. When we walk towards the bird it runs away for a few yards and then turns, still calling, and it is then that it will dip the head as if feeding; the bird does not look alarmed, though I am convinced that the apparent feeding is pretence. No two birds could differ more than the Oyster-catcher and Redshank, though both are waders. The first is ever on the alert, its mate perched at some distance away, but in a position which commands a wide view; when the nest is approached it slips quietly away. Then the two birds will stand a long way apart, and either give occasional pipes, which the crouching youngsters no doubt interpret as "lie still," or pretend to be quite unconcerned. They will preen their plumage, feed, or fly off in chase of some passing Gull, for the Oyster-catcher is very fierce in its mobbing of any birds that pass near its territory, attacking the Peregrine or the innocent Curlew without discriminating. The Redshank on the other hand begins noisy yelpings, flying round and round, long before we are anywhere near the nest, and the nearer we approach the more excited it becomes ; it never actually attacks.

The ability of the bird to inflict injury does not in any way regulate the ferocity of its attacks in defence of its young. Thus the Great and Blue Tits will remain sitting on the eggs and hiss like little snakes, and will strike with as much vigour as possible at a finger that investigates the contents. I have lifted the Great Tit off its nest. Occasionally the Ring-Ousel will threaten a man, and it will savagely attack a predatory bird, but it lacks the determination of the Mistle-Thrush. Crockett's "butcher boy of the woods" is bold and is a bully, for it will assault other birds when its excuse is less noble than the protection of its young ; I have known it knock a half-starved Redwing out of a tree when competing for winter berries. When defending its young no Crow, Daw, Jay nor Magpie dare stand against its infuriated assaults. I have seen it strike a Jackdaw so violently as to knock it off the branch, and have felt the rush of its wings as it flew screaming at my head. On one occasion a pair defeated a Magpie which had seized one of the nearly fledged young, and all four birds fell to the ground together, when the Pie was glad to retreat and leave its desired meal.

The Common and Arctic Terns, and even the Little Tern, will threaten a human intruder and, as already shown, will kill anything small enough to be attacked. The Tern hovers over a victim for a moment, and plunges down with half-closed wings, checking its descent as it strikes with its pointed bill. I have found the skulls of young rabbits pitted with bill marks. When a man is attacked it usually shears off when close to his head, but a friend of mine who has spent many hours in a colony of Common Terns has often been struck on the head.

RING-OUSEL.

Female screening young from the sun.

A Heron, a Gull, or other large bird, capable of destroying a Tern by a stroke of the powerful bill, will be chased, screaming, over the ternery by crowds of indignant Terns. I have seen Blackheaded Gulls hunt a Heron away in the same manner, and this bird will threaten to strike a man in exactly the same way as the Tern, diving through the air with angry cries.

Owls will attack, and can deliver a very nasty blow with the foot. I have known of many cases when a man's hat has been knocked off, and even snatched from his head. On one occasion a young Tawny was enjoying its first view of the world and was perched, blinking, in a fruit tree. About fifty yards away the parent sat bolt upright on a branch, her side pressed against the bole of a tall tree. Her sleepy eyes were half closed, and, though her face was turned towards us, she did not seem much interested in her infant. A boy climbed the fruit tree to reach the woolly babe, and just when he stretched out his arm to grasp it, the mother left the tree, and swooping with rapid and direct flight would have struck him had I not interposed my stick.

The Peregrine Falcon is a bird that can knock the head off a flying duck with its powerful hind claw, and if it struck a man could inflict an ugly wound, but I have never known the bird even threaten me when I have been near the young, and as a rule both tiercel and falcon fly round at a safe distance, chattering in anger but taking no more serious steps to defend the young. The powerful Buzzard wheels overhead, mewing piteously, if its nest is threatened, but remains well out of gunshot. It is true that there are exceptions, for individual variation occurs in the characters as well as the plumages of birds, and there were recently in the Lake District at least one Peregrine and one Buzzard which by their menacing attacks put many scared tourists to flight. I never heard that these birds ever struck anyone. As a rule, however, the raptorial birds keep out of danger, however fiercely they may call.

There are certain habits of Terns, Blackheaded Gulls and perhaps other birds that nest in colonies, which cannot be associated with active defence of the young, but may have origin in a desire to draw the attention of a predatory visitor from the colony. The birds will be engaged in feeding the young, brooding them or standing on guard, and the air is full of the ordinary amicable calls of peace, when suddenly, and without any visible cause, a hush falls over the whole colony, and every bird rises and flies off in one direction, often to a considerable distance. The sudden hush in the midst of clamour is most impressive. In a few minutes two or three birds straggle back, calling the ordinary notes, not alarm notes, and very quickly the others follow and all becomes normal once more. I have seen this unexplained performance in colonies of Common, Arctic and Roseate Terns, and in the Blackheaded gulleries. No dangerous hawk or other bird passed, and so far as I could make out no bird had given a warning signal; the exodus seemed to be caused by some psychic impulse that influenced every bird at the same moment.

The fact that the whole of the season when domestic duties demand attention is spent by most drakes in little bachelor parties has been alluded to; the drakes of most of the duck family take neither share in hatching the eggs nor in tending the brood. It is only fair to the Sheld-duck to say that it is a very noticeable exception to this rule. The parents are very similar in plumage, though the drake can always be distinguished by the heavier red knob on his beak, but it does not appear that he finds this a reason for a spell in the stuffy burrow. Hudson shows how he leads the female to the entrance of the burrow, intimating that she has been long enough away from the eggs, and almost forces her to go in and do her duty, but when he has got rid of her he goes off to meetings of other grass widowers on level spots on the dunes or on the beach. When, however, the time arrives for the brood to be conducted seaward he is most assiduous in his attentions, and ever after that may take care of the brood—or he may not.

The reason of this last remark is that the Sheld-duck has one most remarkable habit, which, so far as I know, is only shared by one or two other ducks, the Eider for instance, and, I believe, the Red-breasted Merganser, though I cannot answer for the last from personal experience. One pair of birds, male and female, will take charge of more than one brood, the second not being an earlier brood of their own but the property of another pair. So far as is known the Sheld-duck has only one brood per season, but I have known pairs conducting parties of twenty, forty and over sixty young, of two or three visible differences in size. Whether the birds are passionately fond of children, and abduct or adopt the little ones they can steal or borrow, or whether there is some amicable arrangement of nursery schools are problems still to be solved, but the fact remains that when one pair are toiling with their own and borrowed infants, mature birds, unattended by any young, are feeding and sporting together in flocks. It would appear that the maternal instincts are well developed in some individuals and degenerate in others.

I have referred to the habit of the Sheld-duck of conducting its young from the burrow to the shore, and it is when this is in progress that many of the infants are captured and reared as ornamental water-fowl. One pair that came under my observation for a number of years nested annually on the bank of an inland lake some ten miles from the nearest salt water, yet every year the parents led them seaward. One brood found a cul-de-sac in a stable yard, and another was last seen on a pond at the side of a busy high road; I should doubt if any ever reached the haven they desired, for surely the food-yolk would not suffice for so long a tramp for such small feet.

Young ducks when suddenly alarmed scatter in all directions; they seem to know that there is safety for some if the attacker is puzzled by numbers; this is what happens when the old birds strive to call attention to their sham disability. Perhaps this is the wise course for all large broods, as it certainly is what happens with the young of the Willow-Wren and Chiffchaff, and with the big families of game birds. Grouse and Red-legged Partridges fly off and leave the young, and these at once scuttle off in all directions, hiding in the herbage, and the mature Common Partridge usually leaves her charges in the same way, though on one well-remembered instance I stepped unwittingly amongst a brood, and whilst they were scattering the old bird sprang at me, actually striking my leg.

Many birds show wonderful ingenuity in reaching the nest unseen, though they forget that constant use of one hidden pathway is apt to convert it into a visible track. The road by which the Stonechat reaches the nest is often distinct, but the track of the Hedge-Sparrow to her nest in the hedge is invisible, though just as regularly followed. The fact is that she has a series of stepping twigs, a regular ladder, and as she hops from one to the other she leaves no trace behind. Some birds, which nest in dense vegetation, will give away the situation of the nest by their very anxiety; it is not by their calls but by their habit of coming to see if the intruder is still about. The Bearded Tit, whose nest is in the litter at the base of the reed stems, would be unnoticed did it not constantly climb to the top of a reed to

BUZZARDS.

take a look round; it immediately drops out of sight again, but the observer has only to remain still for a few moments and up it comes once more in another place. The Sedge- and Reed-Warblers do not as a rule come to the top of the stems, but hopping from reed to reed peep at the visitor and then vanish at once. The Dartford Warbler with crest erect and elevated tail comes to the top of its furze bush home, glances at the observer, and is off again into the gloom; it is elusive but inquisitive.

The Tree-Creeper has a regular pathway up the trunk to its home behind the loose bark, and it is usually a circuitous route, for it likes to know who or what is in its neighbourhood before it enters. Almost without exception it enters from above, running down to the nest, though there may be a more direct way of slipping in sideways. There are several duties to be performed by the birds in charge of young, and it is in the execution of these domestic labours that the old birds are obliged to expose themselves to sight. One duty, that of keeping the brood warm, entails little danger; on a wet or cold day the young are frequently covered, but the bird must go out occasionally to get supplies. It must also keep the nest clean, and when it is flying off with refuse in its beak it is often visible. Creepers and Wrens carry the unwanted matter to a distance before they drop it; no tell-tale litter must give away the site of the nest. When Tits are excavating holes in trees they carry the chips to a distance before they drop them, but the Wood-peckers are more untidy in their habits and an occupied Wood-pecker's hole may be discovered by the litter of chips at the foot of the tree.

Certain birds convey their young to a new site if the old one is threatened. Miss E. L. Turner has given a most interesting account of the removal of a whole nestful of chipping eggs by a pair of Water-rails. The Woodcock, however, is perhaps the only bird that regularly carries its young to and from the feeding ground. The way in which the bird accomplishes this has been the subject of much discussion, but I have shown élsewhere that more than one method is adopted. The young may be carried between the thighs or in the feet, or they may be held between the depressed beak and the feet.

The actions and attitudes of birds when they are uncertain about the intentions of an observer are interesting and sometimes rather amusing. When the Bittern on heavy wing drops in the reed-bed it does not at once stalk to the nest. It stands with bill pointing upwards, the lines of its streaked brown sporran melting into the surroundings; without shifting its feet or body, the neck is slowly turned, so that the bird gets a view in all directions; then it sinks deliberately out of sight, and crouching low makes its sinuous journey amongst the forest of stems. Where it is possible to look over a cliff edge and watch the Cormorant colony, we see the ungainly birds with their green eyes fixed upon us, their long snaky necks swaying in indecision as to what this intrusion implies. They are safe, they know, for the ledges are out of reach except by rope or ladder, and if we cast a pebble towards them they merely swing their necks over to watch its fall. The Kittiwakes on their better selected ledges pay even less attention, and we sit and watch the delightful courtesy of the male when he comes to take his turn upon the eggs, or to bring an offering of food. He bows, he kisses his mate by gently wringing her responsive beak, and whenever he arrives calls, as he swings up to the ledge, the cheery welcome from which he gets his name—" kittiwa-a-ke, kittiwa-a-ke."

On the slopes the wise Puffins stand—they do not sit on the tarsus like a Guillemot—watching our approach, but they make

Sheld-Ducks.

no effort to give warning to the sitting mate in the burrow. They rise in a cloud and wheel round overhead or drop towards the water if we approach too near, but so long as we keep at a distance, merely regard us with wondering eyes. Our footfall on the tunnel-riddled turf may drive the sitters from their holes, and they fly off straight to sea, but most remain indoors, trusting to the depth of the burrows, the chances that amongst so many their home will remain unmolested, and their ability to greet an intruding hand with a savage nip from that many coloured horny beak.

Amongst British birds there is a general rule that the female takes the major share of all domestic matters; she does much of the nest building, most of the sitting, and the after care of the brood. Birds of the Ostrich family are exceptions to this rule, and in Britain the Phalaropes have effeminate males, if it may be so expressed. The females are more brightly coloured than the males, and do nearly all the courting, and the males, when the eggs are laid, attend to most of the incubation and care of the young. It is affirmed by some that this is also the case with the Dotterel, but it is not proved.

G

CHAPTER VIII

FOOD AND FEEDING

THE Food of birds has been the subject of much discussion, and it is only of late years that economic zoologists have made systematic attempts by investigation of food-crops and stomachs to discover the truth. Very roughly, birds may be classed as carnivorous or raptorial, fish-eaters, insectivorous, and grain-eaters or seed-eaters. But these divisions are unsatisfactory for many reasons. The flesh-eaters may be useful to other species or harmful, and they may confine their attention to vertebrate flesh or destroy large quantities of insects.

The Osprey is rightly classed with the flesh-eating diurnal birds of prey, but it feeds entirely upon fish. The White-tailed Eagle eats both flesh and fish. The Buzzard, a bird by no means distantly related to the Eagles, is said to enjoy carrion as much as fresh meat, and when discovered devouring dead lambs on the fells has earned a reputation for sheep slaughter which it does not deserve. Small birds and mammals it will certainly kill, but some of its champions affirm that it takes nothing larger than a mouse; I have, however, found a fresh-killed rabbit in its nest. Its cast-up pellets, moreover, show from the abundance of the wing-cases or elytra of beetles, that insects are a favourite food, and I have enjoyed watching the great bird hunting for these on the slopes.

In this chapter we are more concerned with what the parent birds give to their young than upon what they subsist

90

themselves, and in forming conclusions about the economic value of birds, that is to say their value in so far as it affects our food supply, it should be remembered that at the time when they are busiest supplying the needs of numerous young, the food is not always normal.

The term "insectivorous" does not mean that a bird feeds entirely upon insects, for all sorts of invertebrates are eaten; worms and spiders, for instance, are largely included in the menu of the insectivorous species. Seed-eaters undoubtedly feed their young to a great extent upon insect food, though there are exceptions, for the Twite, the moorland Linnet, will fill its young with the seeds of the upland grasses. It is, too, almost impossible to dogmatise on this point, for a large number of seed-eating species, such as the Linnet, Greenfinch, and Reed-Bunting, feed their young by what is termed regurgitation, and the white, pulpy mixture which they bring up from their stomachs, peptonised by semi-digestion, might consist of either animal or vegetable matter, and probably includes both.

Very many young birds are fed on disgorged or regurgitated food, and the appearance of the bird which is in the act of returning the food that it has swallowed is suggestive of a rather unpleasant method of attending to one's maternal duties. The bird's throat may be seen working as the food comes from crop or stomach, and then appears, a pulp, between the mandibles. A little at a time is given to each expectant infant. The Gulls feed the young upon disgorged food, and as it consists of fish and offal, it is an unsavoury mess; but the young Herring-Gulls thrive on this food, though if handled they are apt to return it, in a still more objectionable condition, for a second time. Petrels feed their sooty babes on disgorged food, but it is a clear and by no means unpleasant oily fluid, largely consisting, it is believed, of the oily squids and small cephalopods which the birds pick up when these are floating at the surface.

Manx Shearwaters also feed on these cuttles, and will dive in great excitement when they find a shoal just below the surface of the water. " Pigeon's milk " is simply the half digested semi-liquid food that is supplied to young Doves of various kinds.

The Peregrine, Merlin and other Falcons alter their methods of feeding the young as they grow older and better able to digest. When the little ones are very young, the old bird pulls off the head of its victim and swallows that itself, for the skull might choke the nestling. The dead Pipit, the favourite quarry of the Merlin, is plucked and then " butchered " into small pieces, and the liver and other tasty morsels are what are first presented for the delicate digestions of the young. Later, in the presence of the now seeing young, the quarry is roughly torn to bits and " handed round," and last of all it is dropped whole amongst the brood for them to struggle with themselves ; it is all part of their education.

Owls at a very early age swallow their food whole, and it is no unusual thing to see an infant Tawny with the tail of a fair-sized mouse hanging out of its beak, as it waits until digestion has softened the anterior portion of the body. I have known quite a young Owl to swallow, by slow degrees, a full sized rat, but in that case the hind legs were too much for it, and when finally it disgorged the undigested parts the pelvic girdle and legs of the rat had not been consumed.

The Shrikes, which, though passerine, share many of the raptorial habits, are experts at butchering, for they hang the prey on a hook whilst they dismember it. A sharp thorn is the usual object from which the fledgling, shrew, or insect is suspended, and when it is a young bird that has been caught the thorn is

TAWNY OWL AND YOUNG.

driven through its skull or neck. But the introduction of barbed wire has provided the Red-backed Shrike with more handy shambles, and remnants of butchered victims may be found on any wire near a nest, though the term " larder " is misleading. The prey is spiked for convenience in preparing it for the young, not to preserve it for future use.

Some of the fish-eating birds bring their captured prey to the young quite fresh and in no way prepared for juvenile digestion, but fish is light diet. The slim sand-eel is favoured by the Terns, and its shape and slippery skin must be very suitable for a small bird with a rather narrow neck ; a full meal will glide easily into the stomach. In the Tern's early infancy the food is given to it direct, but when it grows older the parent drops the fish in front of it, evidently to teach it how to pick up its meal. The old Tern flies in with the glistening fish dangling temptingly from the coral or black bill, and when there are many birds hovering over the colony showers of fish are scattered indiscriminately ; so much so that it has been asserted that communal feeding is a habit, the fish being dropped for any young bird to pick up. A little observation of the birds as they come in, will, I believe, discredit this notion.

Terns, like many other sociable species, do not live in the harmony that should rule in a community, and the outward-bound birds strive to save a journey by robbing those that are coming in with stores ; it is when one bird chases another and attempts aerial robbery, that the hunted Tern calls in expostulation and drops its quarry. The habit of holding a silvery fish by the tail and dangling it in front of another bird is one of the quaint courtship customs of Terns, and it is used with other intentions when the young are being fed ; the old bird swings its attractive bait in front of the downy babe, so as to teach it to grab at the prey.

At the Puffin colony old birds may be seen coming in with their beaks loaded with small fish, arranged side by side, head and tail hanging out. Mr O. V. Alpin estimated that the size of fish brought in varied from three to six inches, and as a number, perhaps half a dozen, are carried up at each excursion we are faced with a problem; how are they retained in the bill during the underwater hunt? It is easy to see that a fish will be killed or disabled by the grip of that strong beak, but when one or two are arranged crosswise in the mouth, the bird must run the risk of losing them when it snaps at another victim. The presence of spines on palate and tongue does not entirely satisfy us, for these can be found in birds that do not share the habit, and are absent in some birds where they would seem to be useful. A more practical suggestion is that the fish are held in place by the pressure of the tongue, and this is probably the way that insectivorous birds, such as the Robin, Flycatcher and various Warblers, can retain a beakful of small flies, or in the case of the Reed-Bunting, caterpillars, when they are adding to the store to take to the nest. The Razorbill shares with the Puffin the habit of bringing several fish at once, but observation of incoming Guillemots at the ledges proves that a single captive is, at any rate, the rule. Certain writers have affirmed that the Puffin feeds its young by regurgitation, but considering that the act of transference of food from old to young usually takes place in private, deep in a dark burrow, there can have been few actual observations; but when the young are a little older and come, hungry, to the mouth of the burrow, the load is laid upon the ground and the fish given one at a time. Perhaps this is also instruction in the habit of picking up, and the babe may learn to feed itself.

The Cormorant brings in a store of fish after each fishing

trip, but this is much more simple, for the pouch or gullet-wallet of the parent will carry a heavy load of fishy food. In many birds the parent does more than place food in the mouth of the nestling; it thrusts its bill well into the gullet and pumps out the food it has brought. We see this method adopted by the Pigeons, disgorging their "milk," and the Shearwaters and Petrels squirting in their oil; the maternal bill well in the juvenile gullet prevents the liability of waste from spilling over. The action is reversed in the Cormorant and Shag, as well as the Gannet; the young place their heads in the gular pouch and hunt in this fishy lucky-bag for what they can find. E. T. Booth declared that when very juvenile they appeared to vanish entirely within the ample pouch, but others say that at first they are fed upon semi-digested fish-paste. The Gannet does not need to hold its captives with its tongue, and this is as well, for that organ in this bird is the merest rudiment.

Insectivorous birds will bring loads for the brood and dis-tribute the "parcel" amongst the young, giving each a share. The parcel is a neat packet in the ample gape of the Swift, composed of a dense mass of small flies, many of them tiny, black gnats, swept in wholesale in the upper air. When cater-pillars are brought to blind and helpless nestlings they are placed in the gaping mouths, but the young birds at last learn to snap them from the parent's bill, although for long after they could do this they retain the infantile method of asking, flying after the parent, and posing in front of it with open bill and fluttering wings. Quite big Starlings in the brown dress of immaturity will follow the old birds with noisy but wheezy calls, until the parents may well get weary and peck their children, hinting in this way that it is time that they looked after themselves.

When the helpless young are in the nest they require constant feeding, but there are hours when the infants are allowed to rest. As it has been recorded that a pair of Blue Tits paid 475 visits to one brood in the space of 17 hours, it is scarcely surprising that the parents as well as the young require a pause. It is during these peaceful intervals that a curious habit may at times be noted. That occasional covering of the young is necessary to keep them warm and dry has been shown, but often it is too warm for young birds in spring, and in open nests they undoubtedly suffer from heat, and may be killed. In these hot spells the old bird will brood but not rest in the nest cup; she stands with wings partly spread, sheltering the young from the sun's rays, and the way in which she feels the heat during this self-sacrificing act is shown by her open, panting beak. Such adaptation to variable and uncertain conditions is a support to the argument that certain actions of birds are stimulated by something less automatic than instinct; it is of course possible to argue that the effect of cold or heat is appreciated by the parent and that she responds by an instinctive action which heredity and survival of the fittest have shown is necessary to save the young lives, but it is just as reasonable to believe that thought or memory are awakened, and that she actually *thinks* what she shall do for the best.

That certain foods are palatable and others unhealthy or distasteful is well known, and we also know that men of different races not only vary in what they consider pleasant but in their ability to digest; food to one man may be poison to another, and this difference may be racial as well as individual. Exactly the same distinctions may be found in the food of birds. This is very noticeable in the feeding of the young. The fact that many birds can, when mature, grind and digest hard vegetable matter, but are not fed upon it when they are young, has been mentioned,

HEDGE-SPARROWS.

and it is well to realise that the main food of the young of seed-eating species is of an animal nature; insectivorous we call it. The young House-Sparrow might be able to find nourishment in grain, but it thrives better on juicy grubs, and the Linnet may have occasional seeds given to it, but certainly is fed with caterpillars.

Many insects are distinctively coloured, and colour may have value as a protection in more ways than one. Colour and pattern may be useful to hide the insect when it is in certain surroundings —green amongst foliage, grey on a lichen-covered wall, for instance—and these protective colour values help the insect to avoid its enemy the bird, and stimulate keen sight and intelligence in the competition between the eater and the eaten. But there are also colours evolved for protection which have been named "warning colours," for they advertise that their wearer is either distasteful or is provided with retaliatory weapons, and so is best left alone. Yellow and black bands are worn by the caterpillar of the cinnabar moth for the first reason, and by the wasp for the other. There is a further class in which the warning colours are used fraudulently, for edible insects mimic, as it is called, those which it is unwise to eat. The young bird has to learn what it should eat and what is best left alone.

The lesson may be learnt in two ways, by instruction from the parent or by experiment by the young. The old bird knows that certain insects should be avoided, and does not bring these to the young, and it is therefore probable that each generation has to learn the lesson for itself. Probably few of the insects are poisonous, but are either unpleasant to the taste, or in the case of hairy caterpillars liable to irritate the mouth and throat of the bird. The young bird pecks at and perhaps swallows the brightly marked insect and then promptly rejects it, and strives to wipe from the bill the source of annoyance. Memory protects it and any similarly marked insect from future unpleasant experiences. Miss Turner tells me that she has seen a Wheatear feeding its young with cinnabar moths, which, though not marked with the yellow and black warning combination, are scarlet and black, which also implies undesirability. Whites, too, are said to have warning significance. But it is possible that the cinnabar caterpillar may be distasteful and the perfect insect edible, though Poulton classes it as nauseous. He includes with it the slow-flying, similarly bright red burnet moths, which, however, many birds will devour with avidity.

To return to the feeding habits of the Wheatear. When the little fern-chafer is swarming the Wheatear will bring the hard cased beetles to the young as fast as it can carry them, for birds and fish alike relish the " coch-a-bonddu." I watched one bird visiting the nesting hole with beetles every few minutes, and she never pounded them before presenting them, as she will do when she takes a caterpillar. But perhaps she only does this when the nestlings are young and tender. Some birds render the hairy caterpillar fit for baby food by beating it to a jelly, for the hairs do not always save the grub from its foes. The Cuckoo, indeed, enjoys hairy caterpillars, and its stomach is lined with the fine hairs of its abundant victims, but this does not in any way inconvenience it.

Information about the food of the young Crossbill is not very abundant and conclusive, but though the old birds feed largely upon the seeds of Scots fir and other conifers, forcing back the scales on the cones to reach them, they also take insects. It seems probable that the young are fed upon caterpillars or other insects, and for two or three weeks after they leave the nest the straight, uncrossed bill is not so well fitted for cone

Jay.

destruction as that of the mature bird. The bill of the nestling and young bird is slightly hooked, but the mandibles do not cross; therefore, by that law of recapitulation, in which ancestral characters survive in the young, it is probable that the crossed tips are a development to assist in the peculiar method of feeding.

Just as normally vegetarian species will seldom refuse a tasty insect, so insectivorous and omnivorous birds have a weakness for soft fruit. The Starling and Blackbird are very troublesome in pear orchards and the Ring-Ousel will delay its departure from the hills when the rowan berries are plentiful; raspberries, currants and gooseberries attract Blackcaps and Garden-Warblers, as well as Whitethroats, which slip through the meshes of nets designed to keep the larger thieves away. But these troublesome habits are almost confined to the old birds, possibly because there are few fruits ripe when the young are being fed. It is true that I have found young birds in the nets, but they had reached adolescence, and their parents were no longer responsible.

Young Wading birds hunt for their own supplies, and it is unusual to see the old bird give them food. They are, however, looked after and guarded by their elders, and are conducted to places where food may be found. At a very early age the Lapwing and Golden Plover pick up scraps, but how many of these are edible the bird has to discover; it soon learns, perhaps by bitter experience, that certain objects must be avoided. The Ringed Plover conducts its down clad infants to the edge of the tide, and there any small worm, soft shelled mollusc, or sand crustacean will be suitable food. The little one soon learns to race after the receding wave, pick up a morsel, and scuttle back before it is caught by the next incoming wave. Even if it is overtaken it is not greatly inconvenienced, for it is very light, and the wave simply washes it ashore. At a very early age any bird of this group can swim.

The young Bittern is largely fed upon frogs and fish; eels being a favourite food of the old bird, they are brought for the edification of the young, and if they are too large are broken into suitable fillets, sometimes as much as six or nine inches long. The habit of cutting up the food in suitable lengths is common amongst many birds, but it is only in the early days that much trouble is taken. Robins and Thrushes will break up worms for the young, but when the little ones have left the nest they are given such huge portions that it is wonderful that they are not choked.

Although there are many exceptions, the following sequence of methods of feeding the young is the rule. In the early days the food is prepared by the old bird by being reduced to a pulp in her stomach; next it is cut into suitable lengths or pounded on the ground until it is in a soft enough condition to be safely consumed, and last of all it is given to the young either to swallow whole or to break up for itself. After that the young one is left to find its own rations, and soon ceases to interest the parent, so much so that she will actually drive it away. Considering how much she has done for it, and how much sacrificed for its sake, it is really remarkable how soon she tires of it. Other impulses, other instincts overshadow parental love, and when the Swallow or Martin feels that the time has come to depart towards the south, it will, without noticeable regret, leave a late brood of young to starve in the nest. This is not exceptional; it happens every year.

CHAPTER IX

Lessons and Language

So much unreliable nonsense has been written about the education of young birds that it is a very difficult matter to believe the more credible stories. The popular mind wishes to believe that the young receive systematic and intelligent instruction from their elders, and a certain school of scientists refuse to believe that the actions of any creatures in the scale lower than man can have any other interpretation than instinct. These men forget that the working of a force or impulse which they call instinctive, which always does the right thing or brings the desired result at the right time and in the right manner, is far more difficult to explain or understand than the theory that up to a point the animal has reasoning faculties. As a matter of fact instinct is no more infallible than reason, and the instinctive action may lead to disaster. Why cannot we believe that in the more highly developed creatures there is a glimmering of reasoning power, and that the failure of the instinctive action to bring the desired result may lead the creature to attempt some other way? Once this has succeeded, recollection of results may cause the repetition of the methods, and though the brain may not have thought the matter out, it registers a code that enables its owner to do in future what it did before. Birds, I believe, have something more than mere instinct, and the way in which they will face difficult problems and overcome them, supports this view.

Yet I have tried to show in previous chapters that certain of

101

their actions are reflex and instinctive, and the one that has been most discussed in the past has been the power of flight. It is constantly asserted that birds have to be taught to fly. If this is so we are entitled to ask, why should it be necessary? The human infant, it is true, is often assisted in its early efforts to walk, and we pride ourselves that we have taught it. But the child begins life as a quadruped, and even the crawling upon the knees is not the natural action; many young children crawl, instinctively, on hands and toes. If left alone the child tries to stand, helping itself to the upright position by the aid of anything that it can grasp. In time, without any help, the child would walk. The natural mode of progression of the bird is flight, and the wings respond to muscular action and nerve stimuli without any suggestion from parents. The bird if left to itself will, in time, fly.

Many times when ringing young Swallows and House-Martins they have left the nest for the first time in their lives, and without hesitation, launched themselves into space. There was, of course, a momentary loss of level, but a few strokes carried the bird up. In one instance a nestful of Swallows flew from the nest on the top of a beam, just when I was going to place my hand over them; the beam was in a covered passage, but the birds did not blunder against floor, roof or walls, but shot accurately out into the open and at once joined their twittering parents above the outbuildings, flying for some minutes before they rested on the roof-tree. That Swallows, being exceptionally aerial in habits, do not need education has been affirmed, but I have had similar experiences with many other species, including the slow flying Carrion-Crow.

What does happen is not that the old birds teach the young to fly, but that they urge them to make an effort, even by force,

REDSHANK AND YOUNG.

though as a rule by tempting them with food.   If we like to thus express it, the old bird knows that the young one can fly if it will, and wishes to induce it to find this out by experience.   How much imitation comes in we cannot say, but the little bird, looking out of the nest for the parent which it associates with the satisfaction of food, sees this parent approaching through the air ; if it has the power of thinking it no doubt wonders how this is managed. Probably it thinks nothing about it but accepts this as the normal mode of progression ; which it is.

The parental actions may have quite another explanation, and be associated with care of the young rather than with education.   The muscles of the juvenile wings soon tire, and the little bird alights to rest, sometimes on a low bough, some-times on the ground.   It is in danger, and either by thought or instinct the old bird realises this, and immediately by call note or the offer of food tempts it to move to a safer place. It must be remembered that many of these so-called lessons took place when the mature birds were aware of our presence, and therefore were anxious to get the young away.   The marvel is that any of these young ones survive their first attempts at life outside the nest, for the young Thrush will sit, a fat, inert bundle of feathers, blinking at the cat that is stealthily approach-ing, oblivious of the fact that the next minute may be its last.

The young bird that is reared in an elevated nest may be excused for hesitating to take the first aerial plunge ; it feels something stable beneath its body, but it sees nothing to support it except the ground ever so far below.   It does hesitate, and sometimes, so it is stated, the old bird has actually to push it from the nest.   I have never seen this myself, but I have seen a youngster so keen about food that it has overbalanced, and taken its first flight unexpectedly.   Very few, if any, young passerine birds return to the nest after they have left it, but here again an instinctive and untaught action comes into play, for the bird, without any lesson, perches on a twig and roosts there at night.

The bird, at any rate the aquatic and the ground bird, swims naturally. Nearly all animals do. It is a remarkable fact that civilised man, and the more arboreal monkeys, are practically the only animals which cannot swim untaught. The way in which an animal swims is by making the movements that are natural to it in terrestrial locomotion, and so long as it can keep its head above water and its lungs full of air it is safe. Some passerine birds are soon drowned, but that is because they try to fly in or on the water, and their wings get water-logged and soon tire with the unusual resistance. We have seen that the young Dipper can fly under water on its first unexpected plunge. Some birds habitually fly under water, the Penguins for instance, where the wing is modified to act as a flipper or fin, and the Guillemot, Razorbill and Little Auk. But others are quite as expert in the subaqueous progression in chase of their prey when they keep the wings to their sides and propel themselves with feet alone. The Diving Ducks, the Cormorant and Grebes with closed wings row themselves along, both feet striking at once, though when swimming on the surface the legs may be moved alternately. These different methods doubtless come instinctively to the young.

If the young passerine bird hesitates about leaving the nest, because it has had no experience outside this nest, how much more awe inspiring must the roaring surf at the foot of the cliff sound to the infant Guillemot on its narrow ledge. No wonder if it has to be forced to make the plunge. But the education is rough and ready, and corresponds with the brutal manner of teaching swimming that used to be in favour at certain schools: throw the learner into deep water and let him teach himself. There are Guillemot ledges on cliffs where the ground slopes away to the sea, but these are rare. In such places the old birds have been seen to push the young off the ledge and leave them to slither down the slope until they reach the water. But a more usual method is for the old bird to seize the unfortunate by one wing, and, flying out with it until clear of surf and rock, let it drop. This unexpected plunge is not so sudden as would be imagined, for automatically the young bird opens and flutters its wings, and the resistance of the air gives its light body considerable support. It at once takes its first flight, first dive, and first lesson in swimming. Fluttering away from the cliff-face its downward flight takes it diagonally to the water, and there it goes under; but it soon bobs up again and finds that it can float comfortably on the waves. Thereafter, still waited on by one or both parents, it remains at sea, and follows them, plaintively calling for food, until they finally leave it to its own devices. Then its social instincts cause it to join some party, and with them it swims, sleeps on the waves, hunts below them, or flies in strings, until the time when mature, it returns to the rocks. After it has left the ledge its life is pelagic.

The Great Crested Grebe has to do more than this to induce its young one to take the water, for as we have seen the little one much prefers the warmth of the parental back. But even if the mature Grebe does not object to this very practical way of showing filial attachment, it has got to find food for itself and for the young ones. With one or two young ones on its back it will dive to hunt for fish, but naturally the infants are not prepared for this sudden immersion, and they pop up to the

H

surface very much surprised, and, judging from the way in which they hasten after the old one when he or she reappears, rather annoyed. These frequent dips must show them that there is nothing to be feared under the water, and after a time, when they are rather less than half grown, they begin to experiment. I have watched these young birds diving in shallow water close in shore, and no old bird was near to show them how to do it. Hunger was, without doubt, the instructor.

If the young bird is not taught to fly or swim what instruction does it receive? Perhaps the greatest art of the bird is that of nest building. We need not go abroad to see the Tailor-bird stitching its leaves together, or the Weavers making their pendulous homes of basket work; the neatly felted ovoid of the Long-tailed Tit, the grass-bound moss-cup of the Chaffinch, the hammock, suspended by spider silk of the Goldcrest, and the double waterproof house of the Dipper are quite wonderful enough. How does the bird know in what manner to build the nest most suited for its requirements? Certainly it is not taught, for the parents have long since cast it off; it is more than doubtful if they would know their child, or it its parents. Yet we do not find the Goldcrest making a nest like the Wren, or the Wren an open nest like the Thrush. There are surely only two ways in which they can do it without error, work from memory or copy other birds. Memory may help, but I doubt it, for the young one is often very immature when it is turned out into the world; think of the Grebe for instance, or the Lapwing. And has anybody ever seen the unskilled architect watching the construction of the nest of another? One thing is quite certain, that if it came anywhere near the nest the bird on guard, whether male or female, would promptly attack it, for the pair are very jealous of their rights. No, nest building is not taught,

GREAT CRESTED CREBE.

neither is it learnt, though it is quite possible that the first nest that a bird builds is less perfect than those that come after. Nest building, with all its wonderful perfections, is certainly instinctive, and heredity ordains in what form that nest must be made.

In the same way all the tricks and cunning, all the clever acts of concealment and care of nest, eggs and young are as involuntary as the application of the most efficient colouring matter for eggs supplied by the mother's oviduct. She knows what to do no more than an automaton, but she does it well. It is only when some extraordinary circumstance arises that there is, in her sudden change of method, something that suggests reasoning power. It is even dangerous to expect it then.

Cage-bird fanciers always maintain that song has to be learnt, and if by that they mean that it has to be perfected by practice they are probably right, but one bird does not knowingly teach another. The fact that many birds pick up the notes of others of quite distinct species and even different orders, proves that imitation is a powerful factor in perfecting song. But however complete the imitation, specific characteristics are not lost ; the Robin's song is the Robin's song, though it may introduce snatches copied from the Willow-Wren or Thrush. The Starling cleverly imitates the Curlew, the Jackdaw, or the Blackbird, so well indeed that we may be misled, but the typical Starling chatter or whistle enlightens us as to the singer's identity. Down by the pond margin the Sedge-Warbler raises a medley in which we hear the Lark, the Grasshopper-Warbler, and many another species, but there is an undercurrent of notes which belong to the Sedge - Warbler and no other. The Song-Thrush may imitate the Nightingale, the Nightingale the Thrush, but neither can copy all the snatches ; I never heard the Nightingale declare loudly—" did he do it," nor the Thrush attempt that glorious and thrilling crescendo which no other bird can beat.

No bird really sings well until it is mature, for the sexual impetus is needed, but many birds attempt song in their first autumn. Song is, in nearly every case, indeed I believe in all, a development from the call note. The primitive song is a rapid repetition of calls; we hear this in the nuptial notes of many Waders, the Common Sandpiper and Redshank being good examples. It is added to and varied by evolution, but the call note may be detected somewhere in the most elaborate avian music. The young bird will begin in autumn a few notes, little different from its call, and these, rapidly repeated or varied in pitch form its first song efforts. The young Robin begins in autumn, and as it sings throughout the winter is an accomplished musician at a very early date; the young Song-Thrush can repeat quite respectable phrases by mid-winter. Song is perfected by imitation, or by competition, for the male when stirred with nuptial ardour challenges rivals, and no doubt strives to produce the most truculent sounds that his vocal chords permit; he is not trying to sing more beautifully for the sake of charming the feminine ear, but more emphatically to outsing a rival. Listen to the Chaffinches in early spring; can you doubt that they are answering one another? Listen to the wild but delightful outbursts of the Mistle-Thrush in February.

Certain notes or rather their meaning are learnt instinctively by young; these are the notes of warning or caution. It is easy to say that the call note, and the note uttered when the parent is bringing food, will be understood by association, for the connection of sound and satisfaction of a meal will be present in the juvenile's brain at a very early age. But the warning note without knowledge of the reason of its utterance can mean

nothing to the little inexperienced nestling. And yet when the
note is heard the small bird instinctively remains still, crouching
silently. The more instinctive this response the less reason is
there for wasting pity where pity is not needed; fear is as
absent as the knowledge of what there is to fear. A nest
crowded with young Jays, snuggling down to make themselves
as small and inconspicuous as possible, their infantile brown eyes
fixed upon us, may suggest fear, but there is probably no real
terror until they are handled. Then the unexpected restraint,
the unfamiliar feel of the human hand, will rouse terror and the
bird calls in alarm. This brings at once the answering call, the
screeching alarm cry of the mature Jay, a note which stirs the
stillness of the wood and puts every other bird on the alert.

Whether birds understand one another's language we cannot
tell, but without doubt the meaning of certain cries of alarm is
appreciated, for others than the species which uttered them will
flock to the source of origin. The chacking alarm cry of the
Blackbird will bring Starlings, Tits, Robins, Chaffinches and
many other species to join in mobbing an Owl that has ventured
abroad before dark. In all the Crows there is a striking family
resemblance in the long drawn cry of alarm, and other birds
listen when they hear it, for they know that it indicates danger.
The alarm note must not be confused with the warning call,
for this last may be low and musical; the anxious "luit" of the
Willow-Wren is a warning rather than an alarm cry.

The vocal expressions of the emotions in birds are difficult
to interpret; we are apt to judge them by their resemblance to
other sounds. Thus the alarm cry of the Jay sounds as if the
bird was frightened, but its raucous love call is far from suggesting
pleasure. Indeed much of the ordinary woodland language of
the Jay sounds as if the bird was very much annoyed or in

great pain. The Corncrake's monotonous rasp is a nuptial challenge, and perhaps a love song too, but it suggests that the bird is troubled with a sore throat or that it is hoarse with much calling. The Bearded Tit's metallic little clink is a happy note, but it is sounded as either call or warning when it is puzzled and perhaps annoyed by our presence. The Greenfinch has a variety of notes, and its conversational twitter, especially when a number of young birds are travelling in a flock, is very lively and pleasant to hear, and the " pee-wee," also uttered by immature birds, is a cheery little cry, but the drawled rasping note of the male in spring, a song and not a call, is monotonous and harsh to our ears.

In most birds the notes of infancy, which consists of wheezes, whistles or twitters which plainly ask for food, have slight resemblance to the various calls and songs of maturity. There is nothing in the low call of the young Curlew to suggest the wild cry of the bird on the shore, its flight note as it signals to its companions in the darkness, its long bubbling whistle, more often heard on the moor than the mudflat, or its angry bark when the nest is threatened. There is even less in the insistent whistle of the ever hungry young Grebe to recall the deep nuptial growls and repeated calls of "jik, jik," or that queer stringed instrument sound which comes from courting adult birds.

There is a popular notion, entirely erroneous, that the drake or male duck is the only one that quacks. The Mallard drake certainly does utter a loud call that is usually known as the quack, but its tone is quite different from the much more quacking cry of the duck. Indeed, in most of this family the females are the quackers and the males whistle; this is certainly the case with the Wigeon and Teal, where the masculine calls

Moorhen.

are very musical. The curious quack of the duck Teal is chiefly associated with spring, and is an alarm cry when she is disturbed from the neighbourhood of the nest; it becomes also a warning when the young are hatched.

The young Herring-Gull follows its parents about with a whistling and squeaky demand for food, but the old birds have a variety of calls, the loudest of which is the laughing "ho, ho, ho," uttered by the bird when excited by nuptial fervour, or when he sends it as a ringing challenge from the centre of the nesting colony. The tone of anger is very noticeable in the cries of the birds that float overhead when the colony is invaded. Contrasted with the many calls of this large gull is the comparative silence of the Kittiwake, for when it is at sea it seldom utters any sound except an annoyed " kit, kit " if bullied by another more powerful and masterful species, though its love notes at the colony, already referred to, are as suggestive of conjugal felicity as those of any birds.

How much bird calls and cries may be conversational is hard to say, but when the young Tawny Owls are abroad, before their parents have decided to leave them, there is much interchange of low hoots and sharp " ki-wiks " between old and young which suggest an interchange of ideas. The growling responses of Guillemots on the ledges may be interpreted as conversational, but there is no doubt that some of them are expostulatory, for they are in immediate response to the effort of one bird to dislodge another from its stand, an effort that is frequently successful. In the same way Starlings when gathering in the evening put up a medley of twitters which are probably understood as meaning something more than mere evensong, and when, later, the birds are trying to settle for the night, the sudden calls of annoyance when a neighbour jostles two or three of its companions are without doubt unfriendly in their emphasis.

All the various notes the young bird has got to learn, and how many are instinctively acquired or how many understood through their association with events is beyond human ken. Our outlook and the birds' are very far apart.

Finally, there are some calls that the young bird learns and shares in, and which in many species differ so markedly from the calls we know that we cannot identify them with certainty. These are the nocturnal flight calls of migrating birds, mostly waders. We hear them as the travellers pass over in the darkness and some we can identify from their resemblance to the normal calls, but others are very puzzling. The young bird must know them, for by them it keeps touch with its fellow travellers, and of that phase of its life the next chapter will tell something.

CHAPTER X

ADOLESCENCE

At last, in the life of all young birds that survive the perils of infancy, there comes a day when they must sever the maternal apron strings. They must live and act independently. Like Kingsley's "feckless hairy oubit" they may declare :—

> " My Minnie bad me bide at hame until I won my wings ;
> I show her soon my soul's aboon the warks o' creeping things" ;

or, still hankering after the easy methods of obtaining food by incessant begging, may be rudely cast off and driven away by the once patient mother. In either case they are brought face to face with the realities of existence, its struggles, its pains and penalties, and its freedom of action.

Some birds, though not many, prefer the solitary life, and as wanderers without companions become Ishmaelites. Such are the Skuas, pelagic brigands, but even they often hunt in couples. But most birds are sociable, and when the youthful debutant leaves the family it seeks other companions, usually of its own age. Flocking of young birds begins in summer and autumn. Whilst the adult Starlings are busy with second broods, the first broods, all in brown-grey dress, flecked but unspeckled and without the glossy sheen, join forces ; they feed together in the fields, they roost sociably at night, they

113

keep in companies when travelling. A brood of Lapwings joins another brood, and yet another comes to build up the flock; by autumn, when the mature birds become less exclusive, there are communities well established. The white-breasted young Golden Plovers leave the hills before the elders are ready to depart, and in flocks that contain no birds of the previous years arrive on the lowland pastures; thence they may wander to other winter quarters, or remain to consort with the increasing companies of wintering Lapwings. On the shore, often before July is ended, the packs of young Knots arrive from the far north; the immature birds, unguided by experienced elders, have found their way to winter quarters, or are visiting the districts where the regular winterers will settle later, stopping for a few days before taking the longer journey.

Short-tailed young Swallows pass over, trailing south, and for a night or two roost in the reeds beside some pool, or in the osiers of a sewage farm; not one bird amongst them has the long streamers, the outer tail-feathers, which are labels of maturity. Two or three broods of flapper Mallards or other species form a small company upon the lake, keeping apart from those upon whom they depended earlier; and young Chaffinches or other sociable *Passeres* seek food in company in the fields or along the hedgerows. The direction and guidance of the experienced is not sought, and in many cases is not required. As in every crowd there are some who are best fitted to lead, so in these parties of young birds individuals set example, and imitation regulates the behaviour and movements of the flock. We see this in the young Starlings, for they settle in a mob upon the ground to seek food; but one or two birds are more adventurous than the others and strive to keep ahead in order to investigate the food possibilities on ground that is not over-

WHEATEAR.

crowded. These unconsciously direct the movements, for the others imagine that they will find food where these pioneers are working so busily; they bustle after them only to drive the pioneers to advance still further.

The necessity for distribution of all young creatures is one of Nature's laws. If the huge broods of any animals remained in the locality in which they were reared, the area would become fatally congested, for the food supply would not support more than a very few. Nature ordains that a rambling spirit shall take powerful hold upon the young; they must go out into the world, and leave the home land. So we see the caterpillars of garden-tiger and ermine moth racing away from the plants that found them food, hurrying they know not whither, but hurrying to get there before the lethargy of approaching pupation forces them to stop. So the young frogs leave the pond which supplied all their tadpole requirements, and risking boot and wheel, hop across path and road, aiming to get away rather than to reach any known destination. So, too, the young birds are attacked by the same wandering impulse; they must move, they cannot help it.

At the same time that the young are distributing, an even stronger power is working in most birds, a power that influences old and young alike, for with the approach of autumn comes the uncontrollable impulse to migrate. In all birds of the Northern Hemisphere this instinct is to travel in a southerly direction, though it may take a diagonal course towards the east or west, or an even irregular direction to follow the coast, but the line is from northern homes towards winter quarters where temperature and food supply will better suit the requirements of the species. The young need neither instruction nor direction from their elders; instinctively they start, urged in the right direction

by a driving power that they cannot resist.   Most of them start
before the birds that have had previous experience of the routes
are prepared to leave, yet a proportion of the young ones find
the way and survive to return in the following spring.   All do
not return, not by any means, for migration with its many
perils is one of the greatest forces that regulates the numerical
proportions of birds.

Bird life at this stage is a complex in which various forces,
quite beyond the bird's control, are working for biological perfection; the necessity for avoiding the peril of overcrowding is
one, the necessity to seek an area where conditions shall be more
favourable than those in which the bird was reared, and the
inexorable law that only a small proportion of those born into
the world must be permitted to reach maturity.   The effect upon
the young is interesting, though from a sentimental outlook
somewhat sad.

We have seen that our adolescent birds have become sociable,
and they are also impelled to migrate, but they have never
known how to reach the land of promise, and they lack experience.   It is a very beautiful notion that Nature supplies an
infallible knowledge of how to find the way to a hitherto un-
visited land, but the facts do not support any such perfection;
the young may be impelled in a southerly direction but they
have no knowledge of the points of the compass.   So we find
in late summer that young Gulls and Terns are wandering north,
following unreliable leaders perhaps; the recovery of marked
young birds in their first autumn proves that very many take
the wrong road.   With sea-birds this departure from the path
of wisdom does not seriously matter, for the change of temperature may cause them to turn to the right about, or they may
join forces with a southward bound party before it is too late.

But what happens to young passerine birds that travel north or west? In most cases, to use an expression which has recently acquired new meaning, they literally "go west."

Ornithological studies of the islands of the Western Hebrides or to the north of Scotland have proved that many passerine and other birds, find their way to these outposts of our land. Most unexpected discoveries have been made at St Kilda, Fair Island and at the lights on the Scottish islands, and in the majority of cases the birds were young in their first autumn. In my manual on "Migration" I have attempted to show how a stream of migration leaving the Scandinavian shores may, by air currents, be carried round the British Islands by a semi-circular route, and how the weary and lost may have dropped for a temporary refuge on these insular oases. But I believe also that other errors may have influence; the untrained young may unwittingly, perhaps wind-drifted, take a westerly or northerly course; a few see the rocks and islands and fall out, but the bulk travel on and on until unable to fly further; they drop upon the waves and join the great majority that have obeyed the sweeping but necessary law. Some few of these misled birds, at times a large party, will drop upon a passing steamer or other vessel and refuse to leave the temporary resting place. From the deck I have watched a Lark on a foggy day flying round and round a steamer, and making long excursions into the mist to look for land, and at last, when utterly weary, it has dropped upon the boat, remaining on board until land was sighted.

When crossing to Norway a Willow-Wren, southward bound, took refuge in a boat hanging to the davits, and remained there until we took it back to the land whence it had attempted to travel. But such individuals are amongst the lucky few, for boats are not always at hand in the waste of water. That we seldom see the light bodies of these victims of error upon the shore has been argued against the idea of great loss of life on migration, but our shores are not patrolled by ornithologists, and there are many hungry predatory birds and fishes ready to dispose of the fallen. I have seen the east coast tidal litter full of Goldcrests which had failed to make the land.

During the autumnal migration a very large number of the rare birds which are recorded as having been shot or seen in unexpected places on the coast or inland are immature. Indeed, it is a rule for these to be young and inexperienced, and this may mean one of two things, either that the birds were lost and had taken entirely wrong routes, or that they had been travelling with others and had, through inability to keep up, alighted for a rest. Whether these young birds will, once having lost touch with their companions, ever find the way again is a question that cannot be answered, for other parties may pass and so help them on when they have recovered their strength.

Solitary examples of immature raptorial birds often appear in unexpected places in autumn, and occasionally they are representatives of more or less sedentary species, such as the White-tailed and Golden Eagles and the Peregrine Falcon. In this case the need for distribution rather than the desire to migrate is the factor, for the young Eagles, Falcons and Hawks cannot be tolerated in a territory where one pair requires the somewhat limited supply of food. The young leave to seek their fortunes elsewhere or are driven away by the pair in possession. These birds are pure wanderers, and if they find a lake, a moor, a forest where there is good hunting and no competitors, they will remain so long as food can be obtained with ease. But migration does influence some of them, though vicariously, for

YOUNG WILLOW-WRENS.

the young Peregrine, the "passage-hawk" of the falconer, will travel with the hosts of southward - bound waders, finding his food supply always at hand. So too the Merlin waits upon the Redwing flocks, keeping unwelcome company with their migrating horde; it has no home, and wherever they go will suit it; one of the number can be captured when hunger calls.

Young birds that are not gregarious in after life will travel together for the sake of company; even such unsociable birds as the Cuckoo will seek travelling companions. The young Cuckoo is an exception to the normal rule for migration; indeed, it is exceptional in all its habits. In most birds the young are the first to leave, but the adult Cuckoos begin to go south in July, and the young often delay departure until the beginning of September.

The bird is mature when it is able to mate and reproduce its kind, but the age at which adult plumage is attained is irregular. Thus most small birds are in mature dress and ready to mate in their second year, that is to say in the spring after they were hatched. When rather under twelve months old they have arrived at years of discretion. But in some groups signs of immaturity are visible for two or three years. The raptorial birds are not mature until their third year, or, at any rate, show signs of immaturity until then, and in some cases, the Peregrine is an example, there are certain changes which may be called age marks that are noticeable after the birds have begun to breed. The Heron is mature in dress when three years old, and the Geese, long lived birds, require about the same time. The Gulls, the Cormorant and Gannet may not be mature until their fourth or fifth year. It does not, however, do to be too certain that adult dress and sexual maturity are one and the same thing; some birds will mate before full plumage is attained.

As a general rule, though by no means without exceptions, the dress of the immature but adolescent bird closely corresponds with that of the mature female, and this is particularly so where there are marked masculine adornments or secondary sexual characters. It is in ducks and waders often difficult to distinguish sex by the very distinct markings or colours of after life, and the passerine birds, when young, are even more puzzling. In some of the ducks, for instance the Goldeneye and Merganser, the sexes can be told by the difference in size but not at first by plumage, but in the former the male characters come by degrees, and show in an increasing area of white on the wing, and in the appearance of the white spot on the face. In birds with noticeable patches of white and colour the size of these areas varies, and probably in such birds as the Stonechat, the Yellow-hammer, and the Wigeon the distinctive marks increase with age long after the bird is sexually mature. Stonechats with very small wing patches and narrow collars will mate, and the variation in the richness and amount of yellow on actually mated Yellow-hammers is very remarkable.

The change from the mottled plumage of the Herring-Gull and others of that group is gradual; the browns and greys are slowly replaced by the French grey back and snowy underparts of full dress, but there is also a very noticeable alteration in the colour of bill and legs, and these are brightest when the bird is mature. These transitional gulls puzzle many people, and are hardly recognised as gulls when they are in mottled brown dress. The changes through which the Gannet passes in its long march to maturity are especially interesting, for it begins life almost naked, then gets a thick woolly white garment, but from this

Grey Wagtail.

passes at once to a plumage that is brownish slate speckled with white, and in later years through a series of pied dresses in which the white gradually replaces the blacks and browns, until finally the bird is white with black wing tips and buff-tinged head and neck.

Young birds of the family *Turdidae*, the Thrush group, have their breasts very distinctly spotted, in much the same style as mature Song- and Mistle-Thrushes. The Robin is one of this large and specialised family; in immature dress the breast is mottled rather than spotted, and there are buff streaks and spots on the brown back, very unlike the plumage of the familiar red-breasted bird; after the autumn moult, when the bird is still adolescent, the breast is ruddy but it is neither so bright, nor does the red cover so large an area as when full dress is attained. Brown tips on the breast feathers produce the same speckled appearance in the young Wheatear, another of the family, and similar dark spots appear on the buffish breast of the Nightingale. The spotted breast of immaturity is not, however, the hall-mark of thrushes only, for one of the fly-catchers is known as the Spotted Flycatcher, although the adult bird might with much better descriptive reason be named the Streaked Flycatcher, and, indeed, Pallas, who was the first to give it a name, called it *striata*. If, however, we look at the young bird, spotted above and below, the name will be better appreciated. No bird is more black and white than the male Pied Flycatcher in spring, but here again the young one has a decidedly spotted breast. It is argued, and not without reason, that this pattern or method of decoration is primitive; the young retain an ancestral character.

In the Merlin, Peregrine and many of the *Falconidae*, the underparts of the young birds are boldly streaked longitudin-

I

ally, but when the adult dress is gained the stripes vanish
and bars predominate.   In the Sparrow - Hawk the streaks
are usually confined to the chin and upper breast, and bars
show on the immature dress.   The rule is not invariable, for
that most uncertain plumaged bird, the Buzzard, may all
through life retain streaks, but it rarely shows bars in the juvenile
plumage.

White, greyish white or other light shade are characteristic
of the immature dress of certain birds whose adult plumage is
dark.   The underparts of both Coot and Moorhen are dirty
white, and that of the Cormorant is at first white with mottles
on the breast, and later much purer beneath.   Cormorants with
light breasts have been known to breed, but it cannot be proved
as yet whether the white breast is retained throughout life in
certain individuals, or whether these birds had bred at an early
age.   Young Golden Plovers retain the white breast throughout
the winter, and in this way correspond with the ordinary winter
plumage of the mature bird, and the same applies to another
bird with black underparts when mature and in nuptial plumage, the Dunlin.   But in some of the waders the immature
dress approaches more nearly to the summer than the winter
garb.

The Terns and Gulls retain certain signs of immaturity for
some time after most of their plumage corresponds with that of
the old birds.   A dark mottling of the shoulders is usual in
immature Terns, and in Gulls one of the best signs is the dark
bar across the tip of the tail.   In the Kittiwake the mottles show
in the first plumage, and the head, so snowy in the mature bird,
is grey.   When this dress is lost in the first autumn a very
beautiful plumage is worn for about a year, and for a long time
the " Tarrock " was thought to be a distinct species.   The bird,

though largely grey and white as in mature dress has a dark half collar, and a band of brown, almost black, mottles crosses the wing. The Tarrock is neither sociable nor a hermit; it joins parties of other gulls, whether of its own species or not, but is much addicted to the open sea, and will hunt by itself. Indeed, like many gulls, the habit of consorting with others is mainly due to the abundance of food in certain spots; the bird is sociable for its own convenience.

· Gregarious habits, especially those of the young birds, may be due to several causes, and the idea of congregating at convenient food bases undoubtedly draws many together. Probably a degree of uncertainty about where to go when the family traditions and the guidance of parents have ceased to function also draws young birds together, but there is another powerful factor. There is a feeling of safety in numbers. The young bird, without much exercise of philosophy, may realise that many pairs of eyes are better than one, especially when that one is fixed on the ground in search of food. When there is a sudden attack from some predatory foe there is a very good sporting chance that it will escape being the victim singled out. The Peregrine suddenly swoops, a bolt from the blue, upon the crowded Knots upon the shore; the flock rises and scatters in all directions, but it is five hundred to one, or even five thousand to one that some other bird will be knocked over. Not that the young bird argues this by any reasoning thought, but it is aware of a feeling of safety when many companions surround it.

Two things engage the attention of the immature bird, the search for food and the desire for rest; so far the greatest activities of life are latent; only when it reaches sexual maturity will it engage in some of the most fascinating of all avian actions. It is waiting, and feeding up, and for this reason the young return early to winter quarters and will linger there through the summer when their companions have dispersed to attend to the more serious duties of life. The summering in Britain of birds, especially waders which do not nest here, is due to the fact that most of them are sexually immature; food, and food only, commands their attention; the mature bird thinks more about domestic calls.

GANNET.

1. Naked young.
2. First down.
3. Full down.
4. Brown immature dress.
5. Losing down.
6. Mature bird.

CHAPTER XI

MATURITY

WE have traced the bird from its cradle in the nest to its attainment of maturity. The parent birds had no idea for what they were preparing the nest, why they should lay eggs and so tenderly care for the helpless infant, why finally they should leave it to complete its own education; but Nature had, for the one purpose of Nature is to uphold the species, and provide that enough, but not too many, survive to continue the race.

With maturity comes to the bird a new impulse, a desire that was absent or latent in its earlier days; a desire that is even stronger than that of satisfying the bodily cravings, that in many species overrules the sociable habits, and that forces it to leave winter quarters to trail over the perilous lands and seas towards its home.

The home land of the bird is the land of its birth, and however far it may have wandered during the autumn and winter, spring stimulates it to return. The Swallow that has travelled through Europe, crossed the blue Mediterranean, and followed the waters of the Nile to their source and beyond; which has found in South Africa conditions even more summerlike than those it left in Britain; that has found an abundance of food wherever it went, in northern or southern hemisphere, may not remember where it was hatched, may not feel external vernal

125

signs, but something within it urges it to wing northward. The Arctic Tern may have nested in Greenland, and have wandered to the shores of the Antarctic, but when the time comes it cannot remain there and slowly trails back towards its northern home. The stimulus, whatever we like to call it, is nothing more nor less than Love. The bird is stirred by sexual passion.

Long before German and Austrian ornithologists had perfected a system of marking migratory birds, which we successfully imitated, a few British students of birds had experimented. Over a hundred years ago John Blackwall marked House-Martins that were reared in nests on his house near Manchester. But it was not until the system of ringing was perfected that we learnt where the Storks, the Swallows, the Blackheaded Gulls and many other species went for winter quarters, and even now there is very much unknown. Swallows of the same species as ours were known, during our winter months, in South Africa, and they were seen travelling up and down the Nile Valley in autumn and spring, but no one could say that our Swallows went so far until birds marked with English rings were captured in this southern Colony.

Ringing has taught another fact, and that Blackwall was perhaps the first to discover, that the bird may not only come home to its natal country, but actually to the place in which it was reared. Swallows have been trapped, still wearing their light numbered bracelets, in the very barns and outhouses where they first saw the light; Martins have been taken in mud-nests that were built over the foundations of their original homes. It would of course be absurd to imagine that this always happens, for there are very many that cannot survive the dangers of the double passage, and there are others which owing to that necessity for distribution arc impelled to strike new ground. But the amazing fact remains that some birds travel more than half across the world and return without error to the place whence they started. It is not necessary in this volume to discuss how they do it, and, indeed, such discussion is futile for we do not know. We only know that not only is it possible but that it is a proved fact.

Our young bird, now grown up, has returned to Britain, it it has been abroad; it has returned to the locality whence it departed in summer if it has been merely wandering, with a nomadic company of its own kind, throughout the months of scarcity. Migration may be a long journey or a short one, but nearly every species leaves its birthplace for a spell. It has, it knows not why, an interest in a special locality, and it is not stretching a point too far to guess that an animal gifted with a memory, which we cannot doubt, recognises land marks and surroundings when it sees them once more. In its early days it had many opportunities of making observations; it was very necessary for it to learn the geography of its surroundings, so that it could find its way to and from the best feeding grounds, or the roost. The lie of the land is what it was when it left it, the trees and buildings as a rule little altered during its absence; it finds itself at home.

And now what it wants is a home of its own. Even when birds are paired for life the males seem to come home first; they are the pioneers, and on them devolves the work of staking out a claim The male has to decide what is to be his territory; he has to take possession and maybe fight to hold it; he has to be ready for his mate, or find one if he is still unmated.

Territory, largely owing to Mr H. E. Howard's use of the word in his exposition of the facts, is now accepted as applicable to that region round the future nest which the male bird captures and holds, driving away rivals, and luring to take her share the mate that he desires. It would appear that the acquisition of territory is of even greater importance than the discovery of a mate. A pair of birds without territory are useless. The extent of the territory is regulated by the food supply. Thus a powerful raptorial species such as the Peregrine Falcon will not allow any other pair to settle within miles of its nest. There is not food enough for two pairs of brigands in a restricted area. Fierce aerial battles, when one or perhaps two of these powerful hunters strive to drive away a third, an intruder, are thrilling sights. Each tries to mount above the other so as to deliver that slashing stroke in the lightning stoop; each, well aware, of the danger, swerves from the attack if the rival mounts above it. And so they rise, soaring and stooping, until they are mere specks in the sky, screaming specks, whose angry *heks* drift earthward when they are nigh invisible, until at last the trespasser is driven over the territorial boundary and the pair in possession, still angry and ruffled, beat homewards.

The Sedge-Warbler's bounds may be just beyond its series of lookout posts; there are insects enough for the needs of its family in that small circle of marsh or of the pond margin. The Robin's sacred land may be the garden, and only when an intruder ventures over the fence does the fiery little bird give battle. The Guillemot's is nothing larger than a spot on the ledge, no bigger than it can cover with its two feet, between which the large egg lies lengthways; but its territory for food is communal, the wide sea; there is room and to spare there for all the crowded colony.

YOUNG TREE-CREEPERS.

The colonial, sociable birds, the Rook for example, have a wide area over which they feed that belongs not to the individual pair but to the whole community ; but this is jealously guarded. If the rookery gets too crowded, no fresh pairs are permitted to build, and the nest started by unwanted companions, even if they be children of birds in possession, is destroyed with much clamour and more than a show of force ; the whole colony may raid a newly established rookery and demolish every nest.

Territory decided upon and acquired, the male declares that he is the man in possession, and he does this in song. The sentimentalist loves to think of the male bird as soothing his mate during her domestic activities with sweet music, or of telling his passion in impassioned song ; but there is far more of " here I am, and here I mean to stay " in the song of the male who has fixed his future domicile. Song, however, does begin long before the territory is held or even decided upon, for male birds will often sing on the homeward journey. The Redwings that winter with us nest in Scandinavia, but frequently a few birds will sing before they leave England in spring ; territory can only be present in their mind's eye. The Willow-Wren begins his delightful carol so soon as he reaches the osiers, where on the pink-tinged catkins the early insects are humming ; he sings whilst he feeds though the nest and the territory are to be established miles away. He sings long before he has reached home. The incoming Nightingales will sing when there are far too many in the spinney ; they will sing as, like Robins, they fight for the love of fighting.

Although song in the territory is the declaration of possession, and the challenge to rivals to keep away, it is by no means proved that it has no other meaning. Just as farm-yard cocks answer one another's challenges, and the Partridge in the meadow puts up his head and utters his creaky call, so the singing birds repeat and repeat again their accomplished songs. There may be, there surely is, competitive effort in these songs; a desire to show off the best he can do to attract the most desirable female. There are some who would have us believe that the female makes the first actual advances in response to these musical advertisements of the desirable home, but the courtship performances, generally described as "display," prove that the male strives to lure her by his charms.

Before the territory can be of any permanent value the male must find a mate, and he must woo her, and it is in these advances that we see some of the most interesting episodes of the life of birds and their young. Courtship may consist of various performances, and the first of these is song. By song the bird calls attention to itself. There are birds that delight to sing in sheltered situations, but the number is small. The Nightingale, according to the poet's notions, is typical of a retiring songster, but alas, the poet is seldom an ornithologist. The Nightingale, it is true, nests in a well hidden spot, and sings near the nest until the young are hatched, but the actual perch from which it declaims is as a rule elevated, and well within sight.

The fact that so many people only visualise the Nightingale as a nocturnal songster simply proves that they do not really know its song any better than its habits; when, in Nightingale country, they only hear the bird at night that is because there are no other birds singing with which they can confuse it, for if the Thrush or Sedge-Warbler, or even that night songster the Hedge-Sparrow uplift their inferior voices after dark, these hearers go away quite satisfied that they have heard the deservedly famous singer. From the time of its arrival until the young need attention the Nightingale sings more in the day than at night, but it is so full of fervour that it works overtime and so earns a reputation for purely night music. In southern counties there are many untilled patches where roads meet; a side road meets a main road at right angles, but across the wide road margin are two tracks, one trending in either direction; within these three ways is a triangular patch, often overgrown with brambles, roses, bushes and trees of various kinds; this tangle, seldom trodden by the passers by, who keep to the roads, is just the place that the Nightingale delights to make his territory. Here in the sight of all, but entirely overlooked or even unheard by most who pass, he perches on some central tree or bush and sings throughout the glorious days of May.

The Pied Flycatcher, after a journey much of which is travelled in solitude arrives in the Dales or beside a Cumberland lake or Scottish loch. He finds a likely stump, already bored by decay, and on the tree above or on the branches of one near, pours out his ditty, until his browner mate hears the music and joins him in the selected site. But his song was meant to tell her where he was, or to induce some female to share with him the joys of life.

The Yellow-hammer sings from the hedge top where his gold livery can be seen, the Linnet displays his rosy breast on the summit of the furze bush; the Dipper perches on a stone in mid stream and adds his simple but joyous song to the music of the falling waters; the Stonechat on the bramble, the Wheatear on the knoll, the Ring-Ousel on the grit wall, all sing from places where they desire to be visible. Even the shy Dartford Warbler with crest raised lets himself be seen when his object is to attract the attention of the other sex.

Birds which are seldom classed as singers have their nuptial music, and they do not sing in private. The Redshank with quivering wings sails above the marsh, trilling a true nuptial song, and in his case the dancing flight, rising and falling almost above one spot, is display. The Golden Plover has a similar flight song above the heathery moor, and even the little Dunlin dances when he sings; can we overlook the wonderful spring call of the Lapwing, and its display of aerial mastery? It is one of the earliest and most noticeable of all nuptial performances; the Lapwing is more truly a harbinger of spring than the vaunted Cuckoo or the early Swallow.

The next method by which the male bird seeks to attract attention is by exhibiting his peculiar charms. The examples of this habit that are usually quoted are the performances of birds which it is seldom our good fortune to witness, such as the marvellous display of the chestnut plumes of the Great Bird of Paradise, whose beauties are too freely displayed by those who have no right to wear them. The display of the Great Bustard, a most extraordinary performance, when the bird seems to dislocate its wings and disarrange its white plumes so as to look like anything but a Bustard, or the foolish sham fights of the befrilled and vain Ruffs are often described. But our more abundant species have their tricks and vanities, and they are all worthy of study.

Display is to put it in simple language, showing off. The male has some peculiar specific character, some adornment, some bright colour that is of value as advertisement, and by posture and attitude he strives to show these to the best advantage. He may, when very excited, very full of vigour, display in the hope of attracting attention when no female is visible, but as a rule it is the presence of an unmated female that stimulates his best performances, though he will, all through his earlier mated life, give his mate the benefit of occasional amorous displays. These last, however, are of a rather different nature; they are love passages, and as such lose their competitive value. They are none the less interesting.

CHAPTER XII

MATURITY—*Continued*

COURTSHIP AND DISPLAY

DISPLAY may be stimulated by courtship before mating, or it may be an exhibition of the affection in a paired bird; the manner in which it is performed is little different in either case. The following are a few examples of what takes place in the species which the artist has figured, and a few others.

The Carrion-Crow is as proud of his glossy black garb as if his colours were brilliant, and in bows and postures, with drooping wings and widely expanded tail, he does his best to impress his mate with the same opinion. Most of the crows also display in flight, and the strange twisting headlong dive from a great height, technically known as " shooting," is often part of the nuptial exhibition in this species. With half-closed wings the bird corkscrews earthward, rushing through the air as if anxious to dash himself to pieces, but his wings are unfolded just at the right moment and he alights gracefully. " Rolling " is an aerial gymnastic trick that the Raven indulges in constantly, but it is part of the same love show, and as he is life paired, like the Crow, he frequently exhibits his powers to the admiring mate.

Showy plumage is an asset of the Jay, and when courting he does not neglect to point out the splendours, but he does more, for though in general conversation, even with his mate, his voice

Linnets.

is harsh and unattractive, he will warble sweetly, imitating pleasing sounds, when his objcct is to charm.

Posturing is common amongst the Finches, and they take up positions in which their colour patches or particular markings are visible. The Chaffinch swaying so as to show his wing patch is a common sight, the Twite half turning away from his lady, demonstrates that his lower back is rosy, and the blush of the breast of the cock Linnet is displayed by a full frontal view, or by a sudden flashing flight. The Reed-Bunting stops his stuttering song to expand his tail, exhibiting white outer feathers, and calls attention to his black head and clean white collar by raising the feathers of the scalp. With drooping wings and upraised crest the Yellow-hammer swaggers round the female, a golden dandy.

Family tricks are shown by both Wagtails and Pipits, especially in tail-fanning so as to expose the white border. The long tail of the Grey Wagtail will be trailed and depressed, though in ordinary life it is frequently elevated. All the Pipits have nuptial flights, and the Meadow-Pipit, though less perfect in the art than his cousin of the trees, bounces up into the air and finishes his simple song as he descends with quivering wings. This slow descending flight, with the wings shivered and the tail expanded, is a most beautiful sight in the Grey Wagtail.

The Creeper has no showy plumes to boast of, but its white underparts flash as it races round the trunks after its mate; the ordinary flight is deliberate, the nuptial exercises wonderfully swift. The very short tail of the Wren is made the most of in all his movements, and when he sings his vehement love song every portion of his body quivers; the Wren sings with head, wings, tail and everything. The Dipper, perched on a stone bows and courtesies, but his high flight, when he whistles continually, is calculated to be admired.

Bowing with drooping wings and jerked-up fanned-out tail is as characteristic of the Ring-Ousel's display as that of the Blackbird, and like all the thrushes he is pugnacious, very jealous of both mate and territory. But nuptial duels in front of the female are most marked in the displays of the Wheatear; the bird wants to show how bold and agile he is, and he whirls about in a frenzy in front of his rival, challenging him to come on. As a rule the fights mean very little more than an exhibition; the birds spar with gloves on. In addition the Wheatear has a soaring nuptial flight, in which he is careful to expose the white lower back. Intentional emphasis of the fiery tail is the main endeavour of the displaying Redstart, whilst the Stonechat, with head raised and wings a-quiver, exhibits his wing patch and white collar. Any doubt about the intention of the bird is allayed by the fact that during these actions the particular marks catch our eyes; they become the salient characters however much they are hidden by the feathers in normal movement.

Considering how constantly we see the Robin it is very remarkable how few have witnessed the display, for it is certainly a remarkable performance. As a matter of fact the excited male Robin looks so utterly absurd that it may be excused if it prefers to do its love-making in private. Both head and tail are stiffly raised, so much so that they almost meet above the back, and he hops from bough to bough in this unnatural attitude, puffing out his breast and swaying from side to side in front of the female, evidently to make the most of his coloured shirt front. The Nightingale may indulge in similar absurdities, but what he certainly does is to swing his fanned-out tail from side to side as he faces his mate.

ROBIN. Courtship Display.

When the Dartford Warbler fans his tail the white tips are visible, and he puffs out his throat so as to make the most of the specks on his pink-brown chin. The tail is trailed and swayed; it is not elevated as in the Robin. The Willow-Wren is another bird which under sexual excitement becomes a contortionist; he hunches up his back and droops the spread wings, every feather of head and back uplifted and quivering; then he suddenly becomes a fairy bird when he leaves his perch and floats through the air. From courtship actions, the Hedge-Sparrow has earned its name of "shuffle-wings," and whilst he is shuffling he keeps up a continuous pipe. As might be imagined much of the Long-tailed Tit's performance is caudal; indeed in most passerines the tail, fanned, elevated or swayed, plays an important part. We see this tail swinging action in the Pied Flycatcher, which, except for a few sham fights, does not trouble much about love-making, though once mated is a model husband, always near at hand.

One pleasing habit that is usually most marked after the birds are mated is that of the males feeding the females. The Robin and Hedge-Sparrow constantly present love gifts, and the female with open mouth and fluttering wings receives them with the enthusiasm of youth. The custom is continued after the female is sitting. Whether the gifts are often reciprocal I cannot say, but I have seen a hen Greenfinch feed her mate with regurgitated food. She gave him three portions and he received them with apparent gratitude.

Probably the display of Owls is nocturnal, tor no one seems to have seen it; if it is like their other actions it is ludicrous. There may be no distinct display, for nothing is recorded of the actions of such raptorial species as the Buzzard and Merlin. From my own experiences of Buzzards, however, I should say

K

that much of the courtship takes place at a great altitude. I have watched a pair of evidently amicable birds soaring and wheeling at a great height, and indulging in little sportive darts and dodges ; all the time they mewed contentedly.

Cormorants also take high flights in spring, soaring and wheeling with wings extended and apparently motionless ; they will rise until they are mere specks in the sky. Paired birds will, however, toy with one another's snaky necks, nibbling playfully, and the male bird swings his head back or from side to side, and occasionally opens and clatters his bill in very much the same way that some of the voiceless storks express emotion. The tail, it is stated, is elevated by the Shag when courting but I have not personally seen this in either species. The Gannet, whose actions were carefully observed by Mr Kirkman, has a very elaborate series of wing-raising and bill-fencing actions, which suggest the quaint courtship attitudes of the Great Crested Grebe. The two birds with wings raised and waving, and with tails depressed, strike their bills together by sideways movements of the head, the heavy bills meeting with considerable noise ; or one may simply rub the side of its beak against that of the other. After this bill action the birds will depress the head, rubbing it against the flanks on one side or the other. A similar movement is made by the Grebe, but the wings are not so often raised as they are in the Gannet. Neck dipping is also a characteristic action of courting ducks. When Gannets are sitting, Mr Kirkman tells us, they indulge in rather rough display of affection, the male seizing and shaking the head of the sitter in a way that suggests anything but amiability, and yet the bird so treated appears to appreciate the intention as kindly.

Whatever the Bittern may do in the way of postures, it certainly makes known its presence to either possible mates or rival males in that extraordinary note known as "booming," and booming is indeed a descriptive title. The deep note, repeated five or six times without a distinct pause, and sometimes more, is a loud bovine bellow, but a single note; it can be heard at a great distance, and no doubt the female listens attentively. When three or four are answering each other she may select as a future mate the one with the best voice. We certainly cannot say what influences sexual selection.

Repeated whistles accompany the Teal's courtship performances, and when a duck is swimming in the centre of an admiring crowd of amorous suitors, their combined music is pleasant indeed, for the Teal's whistle is a merry little note. The birds swim round, raising and depressing their necks, and occasionally rising with a convulsive action as if to seat themselves more comfortably. Before the neck is sunk, drawn down into a close curve, the bill will at times be pointed upwards, and it is depressed until the lower mandible rests upon the breast. Sometimes the drakes circle round and round in one spot. The head action has a noticeable result, for the cheek marking, characteristic of the drake, is then conspicuous, and when the birds turn, the white bar on the wing is more than usually noticeable.

The Sheldrake may display upon the water, but I have only seen him make any show when he was on the banks or the dunes. With back curiously humped and neck depressed and stretched, he ambles sideways round the duck; his bows and neck-dipping, similar to the actions of the Teal, are frequent, and when two rival males happen to meet both spring into air, deliver a peck or bite, and then continue the exhibition. The Teal, too, scuffle a bit with open bill when males meet face to face, and occasionally the duck will show her displeasure by chasing off a too ardent admirer.

Bill fencing is not confined to the Gannet, but is one of the most usual of the many nuptial passages of the Great Crested Grebe. As it may occasionally be indulged in in winter it is possible that the birds are life paired, but it is seen at its best when, in early spring, the full courtship garments have been assumed. The two birds will swim towards one another, and then, when face to face, rear themselves up in the water until they appear to be standing on their tails. Very upright, and with breasts almost touching, they extend the frill until the face is framed by a chestnut disc; the ear tufts, as they are called, are raised, and the bills, held at right angles to the stiffly upright neck, are gently struck together. After a few passes one or both birds will suddenly shorten the necks, dropping them in an S curve until the head rests for a second on the shoulders, when they are again shot up to full extent. After a time the birds separate, often both diving, and on coming up once more, swim together and repeat the perform-ance. The courtship notes consist of a series of loud calls which resemble *jik, jik, jik*, with occasional variation to clangs that are not unlike the twang of banjo strings. But the loudest note is a harsh growl, with which the male apparently signals to his mate.

Many eccentric attitudes are assumed, which have been given names, and in one of these the male swims with the head outstretched along the water, and the lower neck awash. The frill and tufts may be expanded and elevated, but when they hang on either side of his long face the effect is very remarkable; the appearance of the drooping tufts entirely alters the bird's expression. Another habit is that of weed dangling. The male dives and brings up a strip of weed, which he takes to the female and swings before her face; doubtless this is courtship by suggestion, the weed expressive of the materials from which the future nest will be constructed. Low flights along the surface are frequent in the pairing season, although the birds are not usually ready to take wing; in these flights the white wing-bar is conspicuous, and more rarely high nuptial flights, in which the pair wheel together with frills expanded, are the order of the day.

The "drumming" of the Snipe, when the bird by a rapid diagonal downward glide produces a bleating note by the vibration of the external tail-feathers, extended outward almost at right angles, is well known as a spring performance, and the "roding" of the Woodcock is the manner in which this bird expresses its emotions. The roding Woodcock flies up and down a glade near the nest or where the nest will be, with slow, almost laboured wing beats; its plumage is puffed out, and its whole appearance altered during these flights, which take place in the early morning or when night is gathering. The bird utters various croaks and calls when roding, and more excited sounds when in competition several are flying rapidly, chasing one another through the trees. On the ground he struts round the female with wing action similar to that of excited game birds.

Flight and song are the only displays of the Golden Plover with which I have had personal experience. The bird has an easy and graceful way of gliding through the air, sometimes descending at a steep angle, and at the same time yodeling a tripple phrase repeated quickly. No one appears to have detected it in a habit that is common in the Lapwing, a habit with similar suggestion of nest building to that shown by the Great Crested Grebe. The male Lapwing not only picks up bits of grass and straw, but in front of the female, places his breast on the ground and revolves, scraping at the same time with his feet, so that he makes an imaginary nest hollow for the edification of his desired partner. During this performance the banded tail is spread and raised, and the chestnut under tail-coverts exposed for the admiration of the aesthetic feminine gaze.

The Redshank, a noisy yelping bird when nervous, which he usually is, shows to best advantage when displaying. With a joyous trilling song it rises with quivering wings; for a few moments it poises or floats at a fair elevation, and then, its wing tips lowered, its wings in a graceful curve, inclines slowly earthward, still singing. Sometimes, when at a height, it allows itself to descend practically perpendicularly, but again ascends and descends, dancing in the air like an ecstatic gnat.

That the Kittiwake is a good husband is very evident from the way in which his mate responds to his amorous remarks and courtly gestures; he is also an ardent but gentle lover, bending towards her and waving his neck from side to side, as he utters his loud and cheerful call. The inside of the mouth is orange, and as the mandibles are opened wide when he calls, the flash of brilliant colour no doubt pleases her. At any rate she responds, answering in similar language, and showing him that she also possesses an attractive mouth. When the birds are sitting the one not thus engaged, it may be of either sex for both sit in turns, will toy with the other's bill or nibble at the snowy plumage. There can be no mistake about the mutual affection.

All the Terns that I have watched share a rather characteristic method of display, the presentation or offering of fish. I have seen it performed before any eggs were laid by Arctic, Common, Roseate, Sandwich and Little Terns, so that it is quite safe to say that it is a family custom. It is continued after the birds are mated, but with one striking difference; in after life

COMMON TERNS. Male offering a fish.

the male simply feeds the female, with considerable ceremony it is true, but he always presents the gift. During courtship he frequently withholds it.

If a colony is visited before the nesting season has actually begun, some birds will be found on the rock, no doubt fixing their territory, but a maze of slender, graceful birds beat to and fro overhead, the air filled with their long and not specially harmonious cries. Many of these birds carry a shining narrow fish dangling from the coral, coral and black, or yellow bill, according to species, and the other birds chase the lucky captor with loud calls. By and by one of the birds, presumably a female, descends to the rock or sands, and the fish bearer drops also, holding the wings stiffly upward for a second after alighting. The female then flattens herself out, raises her head and bill, and uplifts her streamers; the wings are held half open, but are depressed, the long tips usually cross behind the uplifted tail. This is her attitude of supplication, and in an emphatic remark she announces the fact to the courting male. But he is not going to present this important gift, for it is evidently a love offering, without some proof of her fidelity. He alights, dangles the fish before her open mouth, and then rises and takes a short flight round ; he will repeat this several times, and if she grabs he retreats.

One Roseate female I saw snatch three times at a fish, and each time the male drew back; the fourth time she got hold, and there was a short tug of war in which she won. Immediately she flew off, the male chasing, noisily, as if annoyed. It appeared to me from what followed the peaceful acceptance of a gift, that the male waited for some sign that all was well; that she accepted him as her swain, before he allowed her to devour it. The mated birds rubbed bills and preened the other's plumage in much the same way as the Kittiwake. The fish dangling male raised the head stiffly, and elevated the tail in the same manner as the female, but he did not crouch so low. The manes of the Sandwich Terns stood out rather stiffly during the presentation. Nest hollows are actually made during these offerings, for the male paces rather sedately round, and the crouching female, as she follows his actions, scoops out a hollow with breast and feet. In flight, even nuptial flight, the tail streamers are often nearly closed or trail behind as a single pointed tail, but when they are elevated during display the tail is opened wide.

The only special courtship action that I have seen in the Puffin is a dip of the head, the bill being lowered towards the ground rather solemnly and slowly, but there may be other displays when the birds are wheeling in flight round and above the colony.

Marriage by capture seems to be one of the methods of the Moorhen, for the male chases the female rapidly through the vegetation or on the banks. The female, as is the custom of uncivilised man who retains this primitive habit, no doubt allows herself to be overtaken when she has made sufficient show of reluctance. The males fight fiercely and the fights are by no means shams; accidents often happen, even to the breaking of toes and thighs, for the birds fight with beak, wings and feet. There is, however, a more peaceful display, when both birds walk with heads uplifted and tails raised and spread, showing the snowy under tail-coverts; they have then a peculiar self-conscious high-stepping gait, and when I have seen this performance the birds were silent. The explosive calls usually accompany the fights of rivals.

Fighting, fierce fighting, is the way in which the Red-legged

Partridge strives to win renown and a mate, and literally to win his spurs. The bird is well armed, and knows how to fight with the weapons on his feet. How much the female has to say in the choice of a mate is not certain, but she may go to the challenger she thinks most suitable; for the cock challenges, creaking defiance from some elevated position, and a hen is usually not far off. The rival who draws near is attacked, but the Red-leg is a "runner," and if he realises that his opponent is the better bird, he uses his legs to advantage. He can fight with the spurs, but he can run without attacking, and prefers to live for another attempt with a weaker antagonist.

We have reviewed the life of the bird from its beginning to the time when nest building begins once more; the chapter on display might well have been the first. The life of the bird is crowded with incident, and each species follows certain hereditary rules in habits and behaviour. But there is in all birds infinite variation, and it is never safe to say that an individual will do this, or not do that; circumstances may arise which prevent the normal course of affairs, and the bird adapts itself to the changed conditions. There is always something fresh to note, to study, in the behaviour of such versatile animals.

INDEX

PRINTED IN GREAT BRITAIN BY
MORRISON AND GIBB LTD., LONDON AND EDINBURGH